ALGEBRA I

Assignments

Carnegie Learning®
THE COGNITIVE TUTOR® COMPANY

Carnegie Learning®
THE COGNITIVE TUTOR® COMPANY

Pittsburgh, PA
Phone 888.851.7094
Fax 412.690.2444

www.carnegielearning.com

Acknowledgements

We would like to thank those listed below who helped
to prepare the Cognitive Tutor® *Algebra I* Assignments.

Michael and Emily Amick
Claudine Thiem
Michele Covatto
The Carnegie Learning Development Team

ISBN-13 978-1-932409-61-1
ISBN-10 1-932409-61-0
Assignments

Printed in the United States of America
1-2006-VH
2-2006-VH
3-2006-VH
4-2006-VH
5-2006-VH
6-2007-VH
7-2007-VH
8-4/2008-HPS
9-4/2009-HPS
10-7/2009-HPS

Assignment

Name _____ Date _____

Designing a Patio
Patterns and Sequences

Define each term in your own words.

1. sequence

2. term

You are creating a tile design for your bathroom floor.

3. What are the next two terms of the sequence in your tile design? Draw a separate picture for each term.

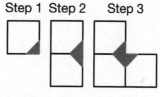

Step 1 Step 2 Step 3

4. Identify the term from your tile design shown at the right.

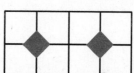

Find the next three terms in the sequence. Use complete sentences to explain how you found your answers.

5. 1, 3, 5, _____ , _____ , _____ , . . .

6. 1, 0.1, 0.01, _____ , _____ , _____ , . . .

7. 28, 24, 20, _____ , _____ , _____ , . . .

8. 2, 4, 8, _____ , _____ , _____ , . . .

9. Create your own sequence of numbers or pictures to challenge your classmates. Write or draw the first three terms. Then write a sentence describing the pattern.

1

Assignment

Name _____ Date _____

Lemonade, Anyone?
Finding the 10th Term of a Sequence

The balance in your savings account is $50. You save $5 each week from your allowance.

1. Complete each statement below to find your savings account balance.

   Balance after 1 week: 50 + 5(___) = _____   Balance after 3 weeks: 50 + 5(___) = _____

   Balance after 2 weeks: 50 + 5(___) = _____   Balance after 10 weeks: 50 + 5(___) = _____

2. Write the sequence of numbers formed by your savings account balance after 1 week, 2 weeks, 3 weeks, and so on.

3. Use a complete sentence to explain what the 10th term of the sequence represents.

While watching the news, you learn that a major cold front is moving into your region of the country. The temperature is currently 40°F, and dropping at a rate of 2°F per hour.

4. Write the sequence of numbers that represents the temperature in 1 hour, 2 hours, 3 hours, and so on.

5. What is the 10th term of the sequence? Use a complete sentence to explain what the 10th term of the sequence represents.

6. Did you multiply or subtract first when determining the terms of the sequence? How would your sequence change if you reversed the order?

Perform the indicated operations. Show your work.

7. $3 + 4(2)$

8. $11 - 2(3)$

9. $42 + 3(2)$

10. $(15 - 3)4 + 2(9)$

11. $15 - 3(4) + 2(9)$

12. $33 - 5(4 + 1)$

Assignment

Name _____ Date _____

Working for the CIA
Using a Sequence to Represent a Problem Situation

A group of engineers is working on a design for a new car. Each member has a separate task that relates to the overall design, but it is important for all group members to understand all parts of the project. The final design is due soon, and it is crucial that all the engineers meet with each other individually to review details before the design is submitted.

1. Find the number of meetings required for 3 engineers to meet with each other individually. What is the number of meetings required for 4 engineers to meet with each other individually? What is the number of meetings required for 6 engineers to meet with each other individually?

2. Find the number of engineers involved in the project if a total of 66 meetings were required. Use complete sentences to explain how found your answer.

3. Describe another problem scenario that can be represented by the sequence in Questions 1 and 2.

You are learning about cell division in science class. Suppose a cell divides one time each minute.

4. The sequence of pictures below represents the cell division over time. Draw the 3rd and 4th terms of the sequence.

1 minute

2 minutes

5. Complete the table below to show the number of cells over time.

Time (minutes)	1	2	3	4	5	6	7
Number of cells	2	4					

6. Write a numerical expression for the number of cells in terms of the time.

Number of cells after 1 minute: 2 = _____

Number of cells after 2 minutes: 4 = _____

Number of cells after 3 minutes: 8 = _____

7. Write an algebraic expression for the number of cells in terms of the time t.

Number of cells after t minutes: _____

Assignment

Name _____ Date _____

Gauss's Formula
Finding the Sum of a Finite Sequence

1. Test to see if Gauss's Formula holds true for the sum of an odd number of numbers.

A gardener expands a small 4-foot by 6-foot garden that currently exists in his backyard. Each day he increases the length and the width of the garden by 2 feet each. He then wants to buy fence to surround his garden to protect it from rabbits.

Day	0	1	2	3	4	n
Width						
Length						
Area						
Perimeter						

2. Fill in the width and length of the garden in the chart above to show how the dimensions change for the first 4 days.

3. Write expressions in the chart for the width and the length of the garden in terms of the number of days n.

4. Fill in the chart for the area of the garden over the first 4 days.

5. Write an expression in the chart for the area of the garden in terms of the number of days n.

6. Fill in the chart for the perimeter of the garden over the first 4 days. (*Hint:* The formula for the perimeter of a rectangle is $P = 2l + 2w$.)

7. Explain why the order of operations is important when using the formula for perimeter.

8. Write an expression in the chart for the perimeter of the garden in terms of the number of days n.

9. The gardener has $125 to buy the fence, which costs $1.25 per foot. Use your expression for the perimeter to find the maximum dimensions of the expanded garden.

10. Find the number of days it takes the gardener to expand the garden to its maximum size.

Assignment

Name _____ Date _____

The Consultant Problem
Using Multiple Representations, Part 2

Complete the conversion.

1. 30 min = _____ hr

2. 150 min = _____ hr

3. 2.75 hr = _____ min

4. 2.3 mi = _____ yd

5. 42 in. = _____ ft

6. 4.2 ft = _____ in.

Write an algebraic equation for each situation. Then identify the dependent and independent variables.

7. A plumber earns $62 for each hour that she works. Let E represent her earnings in dollars for h hours of work.

8. A marathon runner averages 10 miles per hour. Let m represent the distance in miles run in h hours.

9. A seamstress can hem 3 skirts each hour. Let s represent the number of skirts she hems in h hours.

10. You earn $12 for each yard you mow. Let E represent your earnings in dollars for mowing y yards.

Your aunt was recently hired to work for a large law firm. Over the course of her first year, she will work on several projects. She receives a stipend of $3250 for each completed project.

11. What are the two variable quantities in this problem situation?

12. Which variable quantity is the independent variable? Write a sentence explaining your answer.

13. How much money will your aunt make if she completes 5 projects?

14. How many projects did your aunt complete if she earned $32,500?

Assignment

Name _____ Date _____

U.S. Shirts
Using Tables, Graphs, and Equations, Part 1

Define each term in your own words.

1. variable quantity

2. constant quantity

Evaluate each algebraic expression for the value given. Show your work.

3. $8s + 15$ when $s = 20$ 4. $10 - 2m$ when $m = 4$ 5. $\frac{1}{2}r + 30$ when $r = 10$

You want to save money for college. You have already saved $500, and you are able to save $75 each week.

6. If you continue to save money at this rate, what will your total savings be in 3 weeks? What will your total savings be in 10 weeks? What will your total savings be in 6 months? (*Hint:* There are four weeks in one month.)

7. Use a complete sentence to explain how you found the total savings in Question 6.

8. If you continue to save money at this rate, how long will it take you to save $2000? How long will it take you to save $8000? How long will it take you to save $11,750?

9. Use a complete sentence to explain how you found the answers to the number of weeks in Question 8.

10. Complete the table using the data from Questions 6 and 8. Be sure to fill in your labels and units.

Quantity Name

Unit

11. Use the grid below to create a line graph of the data from the table in Question 10. First, choose your bounds and intervals. Be sure to label your graph clearly.

Variable quantity	Lower bound	Upper bound	Interval
Time			
Total savings			

(units)

(label)

(label)   (units)

12. Write an algebraic equation for the problem situation. Use a complete sentence in your answer.

1

Assignment

Name _____   Date _____

Hot Shirts
Using Tables, Graphs, and Equations, Part 2

Estimate the value of each expression.

1. 118 − 22

2. 511 + 293

3. 299 × 0.99

4. 5.26 × 24.74

5. 958.16 + 239.85

6. 39.78 − 14.92

7. Give an example from daily life when estimating skills are important.

8. Your cousin thinks of a number. He multiplies this starting number by 4 and then adds 12 to get 32. What is the starting number? Use a complete sentence to explain how you found your answer.

Great Freights, a local shipping company, bases its charges on the weight of the items being shipped. In addition to charging $.40 per pound, they also charge a one-time fee of $10 to set up a customer's account.

9. How much does Great Freights charge to ship a package that weighs 20 pounds? 50 pounds?

10. Estimate the weight of a package if Great Freights charges the customer $45.

11. Write an algebraic equation for the problem situation. Use a complete sentence in your answer.

12. Explain why an equation may be the most useful way to represent the problem situation.

Assignment

Name _____ Date _____

Comparing U.S. Shirts and Hot Shirts
Comparing Problem Situations Algebraically and Graphically

Two twin brothers, Mike and Mark, are looking for after school jobs. They are both offered jobs at grocery stores. Mike is offered a job at Fresh Foods making $10 per hour. Mark is offered a job at Groovy Groceries making $8 an hour, plus a one-time hiring bonus of $100. Each twin believes that he has been offered the better job.

1. How much does Mike earn at Fresh Foods if he works 20 hours? 40 hours? 60 hours?

2. Use a complete sentence to explain how you found Mike's earnings.

3. How much does Mark earn at Groovy Groceries if he works 20 hours? 40 hours? 60 hours?

4. Use a complete sentence to explain how you found Mark's earnings.

5. Complete the table using the data from the problem and from Questions 1 and 3. Be sure to fill in your units.

Quantity Name Unit	Time worked	Mike's earnings at Fresh Foods	Mark's earnings at Groovy Groceries

6. Use the grid below to create a graph of the data in the table in Question 5. First, choose your bounds and intervals. Be sure to label your graph clearly.

Variable quantity	Lower bound	Upper bound	Interval
Time worked			
Earnings			

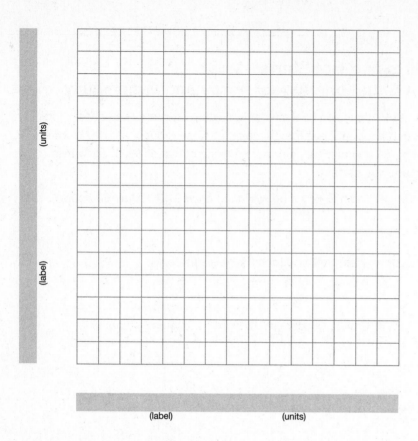

(units)

(label)

(label)   (units)

7. After how many hours will the twins earn the same amount of money? Use complete sentences to explain how you found your answer.

8. Whose job is better, Mike's or Mark's? Use complete sentences to explain your reasoning.

Assignment

Name _____ Date _____

Left-Handed Learners
Using Samples, Ratios, and Proportions to Make Predictions

Define each term in your own words.

1. ratio

2. proportion

3. sample

4. Explain the difference between a ratio and a proportion. Use a complete sentence in your answer.

Read the scenario below. Use the scenario to answer Questions 5 through 13.

A class of 30 Algebra students recently took a test on ratios and proportions. Five students received As, 10 students received Bs, 6 students received Cs, 4 students received Ds, 4 students failed, and 1 student was absent.

Write each ratio by using division and by using a colon. Be sure to include units in your ratios.

5. Number of students who received As to the total number of students

6. Number of students who received As to the number of students who failed

7. Number of students who passed the test to the number of students who failed

8. Number of students who were absent to the number of students who took the test

9. A total of 150 students in a school take Algebra. Use a proportion and the results of the sample class to predict the number of Algebra students in the school who received As. Use a complete sentence in your answer.

10. A total of 20 Algebra students received As. Use a proportion and the results of the sample class to predict the total number of students taking Algebra. Use a complete sentence in your answer.

11. A total of 20 Algebra students received Ds. Use a proportion and the results of the sample class to predict the total number of Algebra students who received Cs. Use a complete sentence in your answer.

12. What sampling method was used to obtain the sample?

13. Describe a sampling method that you could use to obtain a sample of the Algebra students in your school. Is your method biased? Why or why not? Use complete sentences in your answer.

© 2008 Carnegie Learning, Inc.

Assignment

Name _____ Date _____

Making Punch
Ratios, Rates, and Mixture Problems

Three local grocery stores compete for the same customers. They all offer savings cards that claim to save their customers money. The signs below describe each store's offer.

Stop-N-Shop *Save! Save! Save!* Buy $80 worth of groceries and receive $8 off your next bill!	**Food for Thought** *Buy organic and save!* For every $50 that you spend, you save $10 off your next shopping trip!	**Produce Palace** *Stay lean while your wallet stays fat!* Save $15 off your next purchase when you spend $100!

2

1. For each savings card, write a ratio of the money saved to the money spent on groceries.

2. For the Stop-N-Shop, how many dollars do you have to spend for every dollar saved? Show your work and use a complete sentence in your answer.

3. If you shop at Food for Thought, how many dollars do you have to spend for every dollar saved? Show your work and use a complete sentence in your answer.

4. If you go to the Produce Palace, how many dollars do you have to spend for every dollar saved? Show your work and use a complete sentence in your answer.

5. How much would you have to spend at Stop-N-Shop to save $40? Show all your work and use a complete sentence in your answer.

6. How much would you save if you spent $300 on groceries at Food for Thought? Show all your work and use a complete sentence in your answer.

7. How much would you have to spend at Produce Palace to save $120? Show all your work and use a complete sentence in your answer.

8. Which grocery store offers the best deal? Show all of your work and write your answer in a complete sentence

Assignment

Name _____ Date _____

Shadows and Proportions
Proportions and Indirect Measurement

The physics and algebra classes at your school are taking part in an annual paper airplane design competition. Airplanes will be flown from the roof of the school, and a prize will be awarded to the student whose airplane travels furthest from the base of the school building. Before the actual competition, students perform test flights from their classroom windows. Your teacher uses a yardstick, shadows, and a proportion to estimate that the school building is 60 feet tall.

1. Describe how the teacher could have used shadows and proportions to estimate the height of the school building.

2. During a test flight, Jessica throws her airplane from her classroom's first-floor window (10 feet off the ground), and it travels 25 feet. Use a proportion to estimate how far the airplane will travel when she throws it from the roof of the school.

3. During a test flight, Erica throws her airplane from her classroom's second-floor window (20 feet off the ground), and it travels 20 yards. Use a unit rate and a proportion to convert all units to feet. Then use a proportion to estimate how far the airplane will travel when she throws it from the roof of the school.

4. During the actual competition, Andre's airplane flew 120 feet. Estimate the distance that his airplane would have flown during a test flight from his classroom's second-floor window.

5. If Jessica, Erica, and Andre are the finalists in the competition, who should win? Write an equation that models the distance the winning airplane travels in terms of the height from which it is thrown. Let d represent the distance the airplane travels in feet and let h represent the height from which it is thrown.

6. Jessica ends up winning the competition. Does this agree with your answer from Question 5? If not, what factors might account for an incorrect prediction? Use complete sentences in your answer.

Assignment

Name _____ Date _____

TV News Ratings
Ratios and Part-to-Whole Relationships

The new superintendent of a local school district states that her main objective is to increase the students' math scores. One initiative to help achieve this goal is to increase the number of students that attend an after-school tutoring program. By the end of the semester, she would like to have three out of every five students attending the program.

1. In order to meet the goal, how many students must attend the tutoring program if the school enrollment is 200? How many students must attend the tutoring program if the school enrollment is 400? How many students must attend the tutoring program if the school enrollment is 800?

2. Describe how you found your answers to Question 1.

3. One of the elementary schools met their goal when 30 students attended the tutoring program. What is the school's enrollment?

4. One of the middle schools has 400 students enrolled. If 230 students attended the tutoring program at the end of the semester, did they meet their goal? Explain your reasoning.

5. Let s represent the number of students enrolled and let t represent the number of students who attend the tutoring program. Write an equation for t in terms of s.

6. One of the high schools has 500 students enrolled and 275 students attending the tutoring program. A second high school has 740 students enrolled and 333 students attending the tutoring program. Has either high school met the goal? If not, which school is closer to meeting the goal? Use complete sentences to explain your reasoning.

Assignment

Name _____ Date _____

Women at a University
Ratios, Part-to-Part Relationships, and Direct Variation

1. Define *direct variation* in your own words. Use an example in your definition.

Solve each proportion using the means and extremes. Round to the nearest hundrendth, if necessary.

2. $\dfrac{5}{9} = \dfrac{x}{22}$

3. $\dfrac{x}{7} = \dfrac{5}{11}$

4. $\dfrac{0.32}{x} = \dfrac{1}{3}$

In a college calculus class of 30 students, 6 are pre-med majors, 8 are engineering majors, 5 are mathematics majors, 4 are business majors, and the rest are undecided.

Write each part-to-part ratio.

5. Pre-med majors to mathematics majors

6. Mathematics majors to undecided students

7. Engineering majors to non-engineering majors

According to a recent survey, 9 out of 10 parents agree with a plan to remove vending machines that sell soda and sugary snacks from the local schools.

8. What is the ratio of the number of parents who agree to the number of parents who disagree?

9. Let *a* represent the number of parents who agree and let *d* represent the number of parents who disagree. Write an equation for *a* in terms of *d*.

Quantity Name	Number who disagree	Number who agree
Unit	parents	parents
Expression	d	
		9
	50	
		810
	400	

10. Complete the table of values at the right that represents the problem situation.

11. Use the grid below to create a graph of the data from the table in Question 10. First, choose your bounds and intervals. Be sure to label your graph clearly.

Variable quantity	Lower bound	Upper bound	Interval
Number of parents who disagree			
Number of parents who agree			

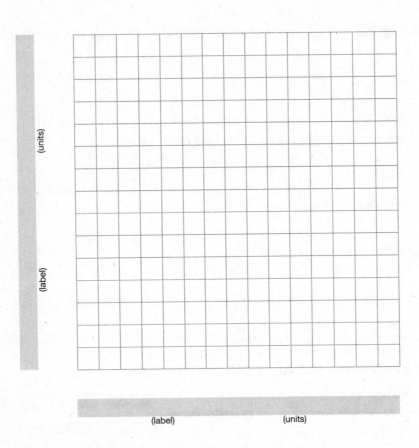

(units)

(label)

(label)   (units)

12. Explain why the equation in Question 9 is a direct variation.

Assignment

Name _____ Date _____

Tipping in a Restaurant
Using Percents

Approximately 76% of ninth graders in the Pittsburgh Public Schools will graduate from high school in four years.

1. How many students will graduate if the number of students starting in the ninth grade is 8000? How many students will graduate if the number of students starting in the ninth grade is 10,000? How many students will graduate if the number of students starting in the ninth grade is 12,000?

2. Describe how proportions were used to solve Question 1. Use complete sentences in your answer.

3. How many students started in ninth grade if the number of graduates is 25,000? How many students started in ninth grade if the number of graduates is 27,500? How many students started in ninth grade if the number of graduates is 30,000?

4. Describe how proportions were used to solve Question 3. Use complete sentences in your answer.

5. Write an equation that can be used to calculate the number of students who will graduate. Let x be the number of ninth graders and y be the number of graduates.

6. Complete the table of values that represents the problem situation.

Quantity Name	Number of ninth graders	Number of graduates
Unit	students	students
Expression	x	
	8,000	
	10,000	
	12,000	

7. Use the grid below to create a graph of the data in the table in Question 6. First, choose your bounds and intervals. Be sure to label your graph clearly.

Variable quantity	Lower bound	Upper bound	Interval
Number of ninth graders			
Number of graduates			

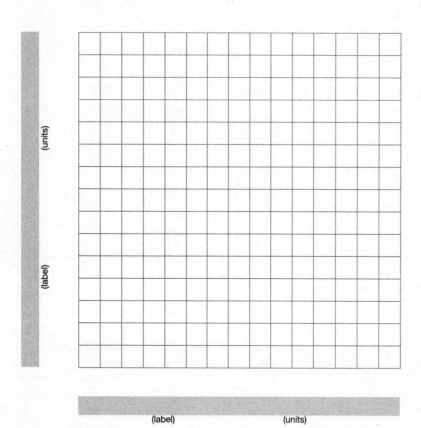

(units)

(label)

(label)   (units)

8. Use your graph in Question 7 to estimate the number of graduates if the number of students starting in ninth grade is 7500.

Assignment

Name _____ Date _____

Taxes Deducted From Your Paycheck
Percents and Taxes

When purchasing an item at a store, a sales tax is generally added to the price of the item. This sales tax varies from state to state, but generally the price is increased by 4 to 7 percent. For this problem situation, assume that the sales tax rate is 6%.

1. How much sales tax will be added to an item that costs $50? How much sales tax will be added to an item that costs $75? How much sales tax will be added to an item that costs $100?

2. Explain how you can use a proportion to solve Question 1. Use complete sentences in your answer.

3. What is the price of an item if the sales tax is $.60? What is the price of an item if the sales tax is $1.20? What is the price of an item if the sales tax is $4.80?

4. Explain how you can use a proportion to solve Question 3. Use complete sentences in your answer.

5. Write an equation that can be used to calculate the sales tax that will be added to the price of an item. Let x be the cost of the item and y be the amount of sales tax paid.

6. Complete the table of values that describes the relationship between the cost of an item and the amount paid in sales tax.

Quantity Name	Cost of item	Amount of sales tax
Unit	dollars	dollars
Expression	x	
	1.50	
	25	
		2.70
		3.30

7. What is the total cost after sales tax if the cost of an item is $120? What is the total cost after sales tax if the cost of an item is $200? What is the total cost after sales tax if the cost of an item is $300?

8. Describe how you found your answers in Question 7. Use a complete sentence in your answer.

9. Write an equation that can be used to calculate the total cost after sales tax. Let x be the cost of an item and y be the total cost after sales tax.

Assignment

Name _____ Date _____

Collecting Road Tolls
Solving One-Step Equations

Solve each one-step equation algebraically. Use mental math to check your answer.

1. $2x = 46$

2. $\dfrac{x}{4} = 10$

3. $3x = 21$

4. $x - 5 = 32$

5. $x + 7 = 13$

6. $4 + x = 11$

You start working part-time after school at a local grocery store. You earn $7.50 per hour.

7. How much money will you earn if you work 1 hour? How much money will you earn if you work 2 hours? How much money will you earn if you work 4 hours? How much money will you earn if you work 5.5 hours?

8. Use complete sentences to explain how you found your answers in Question 7.

9. Let h represent the number of hours worked. Write an algebraic expression that represents the amount of money earned.

10. Write and solve an equation that can be used to find the number of hours you must work to earn $105. Use a complete sentence in your answer.

11. For this problem situation, what are the independent and dependent variables?

Assignment

Name _____ Date _____

Decorating the Math Lab
Solving Two-Step Equations

Solve each equation algebraically.

1. $3x - 1 = 14$

2. $4x + 2 = 22$

3. $\dfrac{x}{3} + 4 = 5$

4. $1 + 2x = 5$

5. $10 = 2x + 4$

6. $\dfrac{x}{2} - 3 = 5$

Your school district is considering a plan to rent rather than buy a new server for its computer network. A server rents for $2.50 per day with a $25 fee for insurance.

7. What is the total cost of renting a server for 30 days? What is the total cost of renting a server for 180 days? What is the total cost of renting a server for 360 days?

8. Use complete sentences to explain how you found your answers in Question 7.

9. Let *d* represent the time rented in days. Write an algebraic expression that represents the total cost of renting a server.

10. Write and solve an equation to find the number of days for which the school district can rent a server for $250? Use a complete sentence in your answer.

11. What inverse operations did you use to solve your equation in Question 10?

12. Write and solve an equation to find the number of days for which the school district can rent a server for $587.50. Use a complete sentence in your answer.

13. During a school board meeting, the technology coordinator for the district states that it would cost $102.50 to rent a server for the month of February. Algebraically, determine if the technology coordinator's statement is true. Use a complete sentence in your answer.

14. Complete the table of values that shows the relationship between the time rented in days and the total cost.

Quantity Name	Time	Total cost
Unit	days	dollars
Expression	d	$2.5d + 25$
	30	
		250
	180	
		587.5
	360	

15. Create a graph of the data from the table to show the relationship between time and total cost. First, choose your bounds and intervals. Be sure to label your graph clearly.

Variable quantity	Lower bound	Upper bound	Interval
Time			
Total cost			

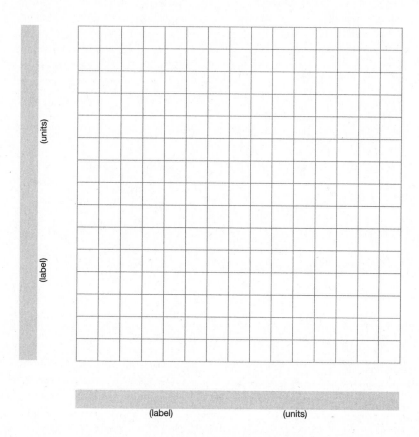

(units)

(label)

(label)   (units)

16. It costs about $1850 to buy a new server. If the school district must get a new server every 2 years, how does the cost of buying a new server compare to the cost of renting one? Use the graph to determine the cost of renting a server for 2 years.

17. Do you think the school district should buy or rent the new server? Use complete sentences to explain your reasoning.

Assignment

Name _____ Date _____

Earning Sales Commission
Using the Percent Equation

Write and solve a percent equation to answer each question. Use a complete sentence in your answer.

1. What is 45% of 400?

2. 7 is 7% of what number?

3. Define *commission* in your own words.

A television salesperson is paid $150 per week, plus a commission of 5% on his total sales for the week.

4. How much money will the salesperson earn if his total sales for the week are $500?
How much money will the salesperson earn if his total sales for the week are $800?
How much money will the salesperson earn if his total sales for the week are $1000?

5. Describe how you found your answers in Question 4. Use complete sentences in your answer.

6. Let *s* represent the salesperson's total sales for a week and let *E* represent his earnings. Write an equation for *E* in terms of *s*.

7. Use your equation to find the salesperson's total sales for the week if his earnings are $300. Show all your work and use a complete sentence in your answer.

8. Complete the table of values that represents the relationship between the salesperson's earnings and his total sales for a week.

Quantity Name	Total sales	Earnings
Unit	dollars	dollars
Expression	s	
	500	
	800	
	1000	
		300

9. Create a graph of the data from the table to show the relationship between total sales and earnings. First, choose your bounds and intervals. Be sure to label your graph clearly.

Variable quantity	Lower bound	Upper bound	Interval
Total sales			
Earnings			

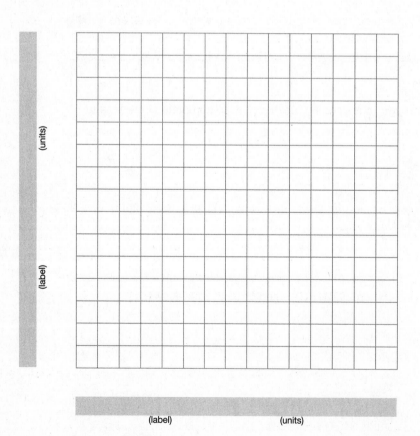

(units)

(label)

(label)   (units)

Assignment

Name _____ Date _____

Cellular Phone Plans from Easy Cell, Emerge-a-Cell, and Safety Cell Using Two-Step Equations, Part 1

You would like to have a cellular phone to use in just case of an emergency, so you compare three pay-as-you-go cellular phone plans. Easy Cell charges a monthly access fee of $5.99 and $.49 per minute for airtime. Emerge-A-Cell charges a monthly access fee of $9.99 and $.29 per minute for airtime. Safety Cell charges $7.99 for monthly access and $.45 per minute for airtime.

1. Determine the cost for the first month for each plan if you use 20 minutes of airtime. Show your work and use complete sentences in your answer.

2. Use complete sentences to explain how you determined the cost for each plan in Question 1.

3. Let t represent the total cost of your first month's cellular phone use in dollars and let m represent the number of airtime minutes used. Write an equation that gives the total cost in terms of the number of airtime minutes used for each of the three cellular phone plans.

4. Complete the table of values that shows the relationship between the total cost and the number of airtime minutes used.

Quantity Name		Easy Cell	Emerge-A-Cell	Safety Cell
	Airtime used	Total cost	Total cost	Total cost
Unit	minutes	dollars	dollars	dollars
Expression	m			
	0			
	10			
	20			
	45			
	50			

5. Create graphs of all three situations to show the relationship between the airtime used and the total cost. First, choose your bounds and intervals. Be sure to label your graphs clearly.

Variable quantity	Lower bound	Upper bound	Interval
Airtime used	0	60	4
Total cost	0	45	3

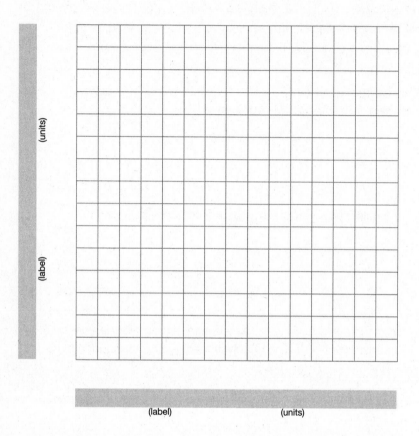

(units)

(label)

(label)   (units)

6. Compare the three cellular phone plans. Identify which plan will cost the least and for which number of airtime minutes. Will the cost ever be the same for all three companies? If so, for which number of airtime minutes? Use complete sentences in your answer.

Assignment

Name _____ Date _____

Plastic Containers
Using Two-Step Equations, Part 2

At the start of a new season, three football players decide to compete to see who will reach 10,000 career rushing yards first. The first player currently has 3500 yards and averages 120 yards per game. The second player currently has 4075 yards and averages 95 yards per game. The third player currently has 5575 yards and averages 80 yards per game. Assume that there are 16 games in one season.

1. If each player gains yards at his current average, how many yards will each have at the end of the season? Show your work and use complete sentences in your answer.

2. Use complete sentences to explain how you determined the yards for each player in Question 1.

3. Let t represent the total rushing yards and let g represent the number of games played. Write an equation that gives the total rushing yards in terms of the number of games played for each of the three players.

4. Complete the table of values that shows the relationship between the total rushing yards and the number of games played.

		First player	Second player	Third player
Quantity Name	Games played	Total yards	Total yards	Total yards
Unit	games	yards	yards	yards
Expression	g			
	0			
	16			
	23			
	40			
	60			

5. Create graphs for all three players to show the relationship between games played and total cost. First, choose your bounds and intervals. Be sure to label your graphs clearly.

Variable quantity	Lower bound	Upper bound	Interval
Games played	0	75	5
Total yards	0	15,000	1000

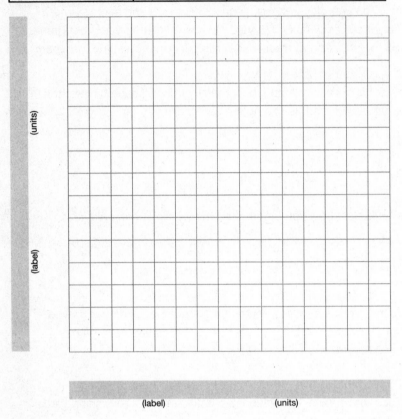

(units)

(label)

(label)   (units)

6. Use the graph to estimate after how many games each player will reach 10,000 total yards.

7. Check your estimate for each player in Question 6 using algebraic equations to find after how many games each player will reach 10,000 yards. Use complete sentences in your answer.

8. Do you think using each player's current average yards per game is a good predictor for determining who will reach the 10,000-yard goal first? Why or why not?

Assignment

Name _____ Date _____

Brrr! It's Cold Out There!
Integers and Integer Operations

Perform each indicated operation.

1. −2 + 5

2. −3 + (−2)

3. 6 + (−8)

4. 8 − 10

5. −3 − (−5)

6. −8 − 2

7. 7(−2)

8. (−3)(−7)

9. (−5)^2

10. −24 ÷ (−3)

11. 64 ÷ (−2)

12. −22 ÷ 11

The equation given in the text that relates a temperature C in degrees Celsius to a temperature F in degrees Fahrenheit is $F = \dfrac{9}{5}C + 32$. By solving for C, another equation that relates these two variable quantities is $C = \dfrac{5}{9}F - \dfrac{160}{9}$.

13. Use the second equation above to find the temperature in degrees Celsius that corresponds to a temperature of −4°F. Show all your work and use a complete sentence in your answer.

14. Use the second equation above to find the temperature in degrees Fahrenheit that corresponds to a temperature of −15°C. Show all your work and use a complete sentence in your answer.

15. Write the second temperature equation above so that the fractions are decimals.

16. Which temperature equation is easier to use? Use complete sentences to explain your answer.

3

Assignment

Name _____ Date _____

Shipwreck at the Bottom of the Sea
The Coordinate Plane

Define each term in your own words.

1. origin

2. *x*-axis

3. *y*-axis

4. ordered pair

5. *x*-coordinate

6. *y*-coordinate

7. Plot and label each point in the coordinate plane.

A(2, –6)

B(0, –4)

C(–4, 0)

D(2, 0)

E(2, 6)

F(–4, 6)

G(–4, –6)

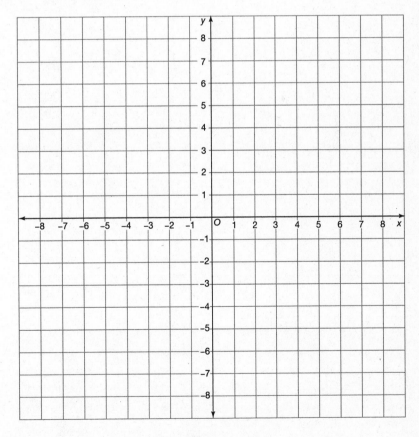

8. What letter is formed when you connect the points you plotted in Question 7 in alphabetical order?

3

Assignment

Name _____ Date _____

Engineering a Highway
Using a Graph of a Two-Step Equation

You are knitting a scarf for your best friend and want to have it finished by 6:00 P.M. You want the scarf to be 60 inches long when it is complete. At 1:00 P.M. you have already knit 15 inches of the scarf, and you estimate that from this point on you can knit at the rate of $\frac{1}{4}$ inch per minute.

1. Write an equation that represents the length of the scarf, in inches, in terms of the number of minutes.

2. Find the length of the scarf at 2:30 P.M. and at 3:20 P.M. Show all your work and use a complete sentence in your answer.

3. What time will it be when you complete the scarf? Show all your work and use a complete sentence in your answer.

4. Assuming you knit at a constant rate, at what time did you begin knitting the scarf? Show all your work and use a complete sentence in your answer.

5. Complete the table of values that shows the relationship between the number of minutes and the length of the scarf in inches.

Quantity Name	Time since 1:00 P.M.	Scarf length
Unit	minutes	inches
Expression	m	
	0	
	90	
	140	
	180	

6. Create a graph of the data from the table to show the relationship between minutes since 1:00 P.M. and the length of the scarf. First, choose your bounds and intervals. Be sure to label your graph clearly.

Variable quantity	Lower bound	Upper bound	Interval
Time since 1:00 P.M.			
Scarf length			

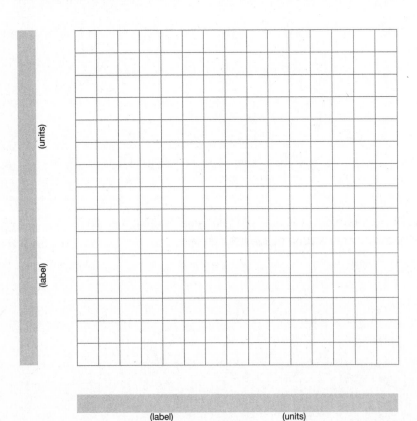

(units)

(label)

(label)   (units)

7. Use the graph in Question 6 to estimate the length of the scarf at 3:30 P.M. Use a complete sentence in your answer.

8. Use the graph in Question 6 to estimate what time it will be when the scarf is 25 inches long. Use a complete sentence in your answer.

Solve each equation.

9. $\dfrac{2}{5}x + 100 = 1100$

10. $\dfrac{3}{4}x - 2 = 10$

11. $-12 = \dfrac{2}{3}x + 2$

3

Assignment

Name _____ Date _____

Up, Up, and Away!
Solving and Graphing Inequalities in One Variable

A big Algebra test is coming up, and you are worried about how it will affect your grade. It will have 40 multiple-choice questions and you would like to know how many questions you will need to answer correctly in order to receive each grade. (For a review of percents, see Chapter 2.).

1. What is the number of questions will you need to answer correctly in order to receive a 90%? What is the number of questions will you need to answer correctly in order to receive an 80%? What is the number of questions will you need to answer correctly in order to receive a 70%? What is the number of questions will you need to answer correctly in order to receive a 60%?

2. Let x represent the number of questions answered correctly. Write inequalities for the number of questions that you need to answer correctly in order to receive an A (90%–100%), a B (80%–89%), a C (70%–79%), a D (60%–69%), or an F (0%–59%).

3. Which letter grades are represented by a compound inequality?

4. Students in one particular class did poorly on the test, so the teacher allowed the students to take the tests home and correct them in order to earn more points. If a student answered 20 questions correctly the first time, what number of additional questions will she need to answer correctly in order to raise her grade to at least a C? Let q represent the number of corrected problems. Show all your work and use a complete sentence in your answer.

Solve each inequality and graph the solution.

5. $x - 3 > 7$

```
<-+---+---+---+---+---+---+->
  7   8   9  10  11  12  13
```

6. $-2x \le 10$

```
<-+---+---+---+---+---+---+->
 -8  -7  -6  -5  -4  -3  -2
```

7. $-3x + 2 \ge 11$

```
<-+---+---+---+---+---+---+->
 -6  -5  -4  -3  -2  -1   0
```

8. $\frac{1}{5}x + 10 < 24$

```
<-+---+---+---+---+---+---+->
 40  50  60  70  80  90 100
```

Assignment

Name _____ Date _____

Moving a Sand Pile
Relations and Functions

Define each term in your own words.

1. domain

2. range

3. function

Decide whether each relation is a function. If the relation is a function, identify the domain and range. If the relation is not a function, explain why not. Use complete sentences in your answer.

4. Relation: {(2, 5), (3, 7), (−1, −1), (5, 11)}

5. Relation: {(1, 1), (2, 1), (3, 2), (3, 3)}

Identify the input and output for each scenario and decide whether or not it represents a function. Use complete sentences to explain your answer.

6. Each student in your class identifies his or her birthday.

7. Each student in your class identifies his or her phone number.

8. At a family reunion, each person writes down his or her home address to create a family directory.

4

Assignment

Name _____ Date _____

Let's Bowl!
Evaluating Functions, Function Notation, Domain, and Range

1. What is the difference between a relation and a function?

2. How do you evaluate a function?

Evaluate each function at the specified value. Show your work.

3. $f(x) = 3 + x$ at $x = -5$ **4.** $f(x) = 2x - 15$ at $x = 7$ **5.** $f(x) = -4 + 3x$ at $x = -1$

You and your friends from Algebra class have volunteered to tutor fifth grade students at the neighborhood elementary school after school. You would like to provide a snack for the fifth graders during tutoring time. You know that you will have to spend $6.50 on napkins and plates. You will be able to buy pretzels and juice at a rate of $.40 per student.

6. Find the total cost of providing snacks if 10 fifth graders come to tutoring. Show your work and use a complete sentence in your answer.

7. Find the total cost of providing snacks if 15 fifth graders come to tutoring. Show your work and use a complete sentence in your answer.

8. Use function notation to write an equation representing the total cost of providing snacks for any number of students.

9. Use complete sentences to explain how to evaluate the function for any number of students.

10. What is the domain of the function in Question 8 if you do not consider the problem situation? Use a complete sentence in your answer.

11. Suppose there are 65 fifth-grade students at the neighborhood elementary school. What is the domain of the function in Question 8 now? Use a complete sentence in your answer.

12. Suppose there are only enough tutors for 12 fifth graders to attend tutoring. What is the domain and range of the function in Question 8 now? Use complete sentences in your answer.

Assignment

Name _____ Date _____

Math Magic
The Distributive Property

Use the distributive property to simplify each algebraic expression.

1. $4(x + 3)$

2. $8(3x - 4)$

3. $10x - 15x$

4. $5(9 - 2x)$

5. $\dfrac{36 - 24x}{6}$

6. $\dfrac{56 + 7x}{7}$

Use the distributive property in reverse to rewrite each algebraic expression.

7. $5x + 80$

8. $7x - 28$

9. $4x + 18$

10. $28x - 49$

11. $-5 - 15x$

12. $4x + 7$

You and two of your friends have decided to start your own company assembling and selling computers. Suppose that you have already sold the first 20 computers that you assembled for $1800 each. You will then sell each additional computer that you assemble for $1800.

13. What will your company's total sales be if you sell 10 additional computers? What will your company's total sales be if you sell 50 additional computers? What will your company's total sales be if you sell 100 additional computers? What will your company's total sales be if you sell 200 additional computers?

14. Write an expression that can be used to calculate your company's total sales. Write your expression in factored form and in simplified form using the distributive property.

15. Write two expressions for the total area of the two rectangular sections of garden. Then find the total area. Show all your work.

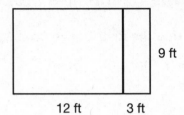

9 ft

12 ft   3 ft

Assignment

Name _____ Date _____

Numbers in Your Everyday Life
Real Numbers and Their Properties

Define each term in your own words.

1. closure

2. rational number

3. irrational number

Determine whether each decimal value is rational or irrational number. If it is a rational number, write it as a fraction.

4. 0.5

5. 0.5555...

6. 0.151155111555...

7. 0.1

8. 0.152542384...

9. 0.151515...

Identify the property illustrated by each statement.

10. $2 = 2$

11. $3(7) = 7(3)$

12. $(4 + 7) + (-2) = 4 + (7 + (-2))$

13. If $\frac{1}{5} = 0.2$ and $0.2 = 20\%$, then $\frac{1}{5} = 20\%$.

14. Identify the property or reason that is used in each step.

$3(5 + 1) - 4 = 5(2 - 8) + 44$ _____

$15 + 3 - 4 = 5(2 - 8) + 44$ _____

$15 + 3 - 4 = 10 - 40 + 44$ _____

$(15 + 3) - 4 = (10 - 40) + 44$ _____

$18 - 4 = -30 + 44$ _____

$14 = 14$ _____

4

Assignment

Name _____ Date _____

Technology Reporter
Solving More Complicated Equations

Solve each equation. Show all your work. Be sure to check your answer in the original equation.

1. $3x = 2x + 5$

2. $3x + 2 = 2x + 4$

3. $-2x + 1 = 3(x + 2)$

4. $5x - 1 = 7(x - 1)$

5. $-x + 4 = -3x + 8$

6. $2(10 + 3x) = 4(x - 4)$

As a member of the local teen community group, you and your friends take on the responsibility to analyze the most economical option for flooring for the new center. After all the bids are collected, the two most promising bids are for vinyl flooring and carpeting. The vinyl flooring costs $31,000 to install, along with a monthly cleaning and maintenance fee of $175. The carpeting costs $22,500 to install along with a monthly cleaning and maintenance fee of $325.

7. What is the cost of vinyl flooring for 1 month? What is the cost of vinyl flooring for 10 months? What is the cost of vinyl flooring for 50 months? What is the cost of vinyl flooring for 60 months?

8. Write an expression for the cost of vinyl flooring.

9. What is the cost of carpeting for 1 month? What is the cost of carpeting for 10 months? What is the cost of carpeting for 50 months? What is the cost of carpeting for 60 months?

10. Write an expression for the cost of carpeting.

11. Complete the table below.

Quantity Name	Time	Cost of vinyl flooring	Cost of carpeting
Unit	months	dollars	dollars
Expression	*m*		
	1		
	10		
	50		
	60		

12. Based on the table, estimate when the cost of the vinyl flooring will equal the cost of the carpeting. Use complete sentences to explain your answer.

13. Write and solve an equation to find when the two flooring options will cost the same. Show all your work and use a complete sentence in your answer.

14. Why is it helpful to isolate the variable *m* on the right side of the equation in Question 13, instead of the left side? Use a complete sentence in your answer.

15. Your group must determine the best option over time. Consider the fact that both products carry a 10-year warranty. Justify your recommendation using your calculations above.

© 2008 Carnegie Learning, Inc.

Assignment

Name _____ Date _____

Rules of Sports
Solving Absolute Value Equations and Inequalities

Evaluate each expression. Show all your work.

1. $|-13 + 5|$

2. $|6 - 10| \cdot (-2)$

3. $|(-5)(2)|$

4. $|-2| + |3|$

5. $|-2 + 3|$

6. $\left| \dfrac{-24}{4} \right|$

7. Complete the table below for the functions $y = x + 2$ and $y = |x + 2|$.

x	x + 2	|x + 2|
−4		
−3		
−2		
−1		
0		
1		
2		

8. Graph both functions from Question 7 on the grid at the right.

9. How does the absolute value change the graph of the function?

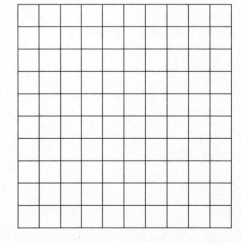

4

Assignment

Name _____ Date _____

Widgets, Dumbbells, and Dumpsters
Multiple Representatives of Linear Functions

Widgets cost $7 each, with a shipping charge of $11 per order.

1. Write an equation for the problem situation. Use w to represent the number of widgets ordered and use c to represent the total cost of an order in dollars.

2. What is the total cost of an order for 12 widgets? What is the total cost of an order for 257 widgets? Show all your work and use a complete sentence in your answer.

3. How many widgets can you order for $88? Show all your work and use a complete sentence in your answer.

4. How many widgets can you order for $1488? Show all your work and use a complete sentence in your answer.

5. How many widgets can you order for $6472? Show all your work and use a complete sentence in your answer.

5

Assignment

Name _____ Date _____

Selling Balloons
Finding Intercepts of a Graph

Overnight, a huge blizzard dumped 10 inches of snow on the ground. When the sun comes out, it melts the snow at a rate of about 1 inch per hour.

1. Write an equation for the problem situation. Use h to represent time in hours and use s to represent the amount of snow on the ground in inches.

2. Complete the table of values that shows the relationship between the amount of snow in inches on the ground and the time in hours.

Quantity Name	Time since sun came out	Snow on the ground
Unit	hours	inches
Expression	h	
	–2	
		9
	5	
		0
	11	

3. Does an h-value of –2 make sense in the problem situation? Use complete sentences to explain.

4. Create a graph of the data from the table to show the relationship between time and the amount of snow on the ground. Use the bounds and intervals given below. Be sure to label your graph clearly.

Variable quantity	Lower bound	Upper bound	Interval
Time	–3	12	1
Snow on the ground	–3	12	1

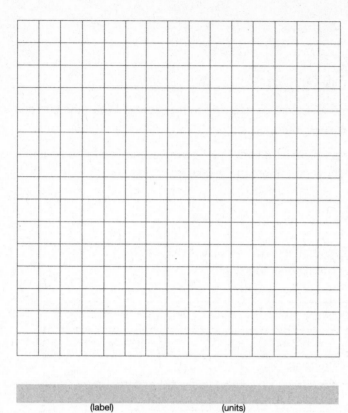

(units)

(label)

(label)   (units)

5. Use the graph in Question 4 to find the *h*- and *s*-intercepts. What do these points tell you about the relationship between the amount of snow on the ground and the time in hours. Use complete sentences in your answer.

6. Algebraically, verify the *h*- and *s*-intercepts you found in Question 5.

5

7. Does the graph in Question 4 increase or decrease from left to right? Why? Use complete sentences in your answer.

Assignment

Name _____ Date _____

Recycling and Saving
Finding the Slope of a Line

The student council is selling heart-shaped lollipops to help raise money for the Valentine's Day dance. They earn $.25 for each lollipop sold.

1. Write an equation that relates the number of lollipops sold to the amount of money earned. Use *x* to represent the number of lollipops sold and *y* to represent the amount of money earned.

2. Create a graph of the equation in Question 1 to show the relationship between the number of lollipops sold and money earned. Use the bounds and intervals given below. Be sure to label your graph clearly.

Variable quantity	Lower bound	Upper bound	Interval
Number of lollipops sold	0	75	5
Money earned	0	30	2

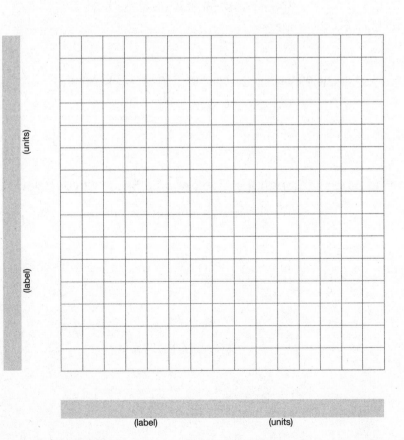

(units)

(label)

(label)   (units)

3. Use your graph to find the increase in earnings when the number of lollipops sold increases by one. Use a complete sentence in your answer.

4. Use your graph to find the increase in earnings when the number of lollipops sold increases by 20. Use a complete sentence in your answer.

5. Use your graph to find the increase in earnings when the number of lollipops sold increases by 45. Use a complete sentence in your answer.

6. Write a unit rate that compares the increase in earnings to the increase in the number of lollipops sold.

7. Determine whether the slope of the line in Question 2 is positive, negative, zero, or undefined. Complete each sentence to explain.

The rise of the line is a _____ number and the run of the line is _____ number. So, the slope is _____.

8. Use the slope formula and two points on the line in Question 2 to verify the slope in Question 6.

Find the slope of the line that passes through the given points. Show all your work.

9. (5, 7) and (6, 5)

10. (20, 50) and (60, 90)

5

Assignment

Name _____ Date _____

Running a Marathon
Slope-Intercept Form

Write each equation in slope-intercept form, if necessary. Then identify the slope and *y*-intercept.

1. $y = 2x + 3.5$

2. $y = -3(x - 5)$

3. $y = \frac{1}{4}x - 10$

Two families are competing on a reality TV show. The goal of the show is to race across the country from Los Angeles, California to New York, New York. The families are taking indirect routes and have different tasks to complete along the way. The family that accomplishes all of their tasks and finishes the race in the least amount of time wins.

4. The race has begun and the first family has traveled 450 miles. They are averaging 300 miles per day. Write an equation that gives the total distance the first family has traveled in terms of the number of days that have passed after the first 450 miles were completed. Use *x* to represent the number of days and *y* to represent the total distance traveled in miles.

5. If the first family continues traveling at this rate, how far will they have traveled 4 days after the first 450 miles are completed? Show all your work and use a complete sentence in your answer.

6. If the first family continues traveling at this rate, how many additional days will it take them to travel 1950 total miles after the first 450 miles are completed? Show all your work and use a complete sentence in your answer.

7. The race has begun and the second family has traveled 1100 miles. They are currently traveling at an average rate of 150 miles per day. Write an equation that gives the total distance the second family has traveled in terms of the number of days that have passed after the first 1100 miles were completed. Use *x* to represent the number of days and *y* to represent the total distance traveled in miles.

5

8. If the second family continues traveling at this rate, how far will they have traveled 5 days after the first 1100 miles are completed? Show all your work and use a complete sentence in your answer.

9. If the second family continues traveling at this rate, how many additional days will it take them to travel 1700 total miles after the first 1100 miles are completed? Show all your work and use a complete sentence in your answer.

10. Identify the slope and *y*-intercept for each equation in Questions 4 and 7.

11. Create graphs of the equations in Questions 4 and 7 to show the relationship between time and total distance. Use the slopes and *y*-intercepts from Question 10.

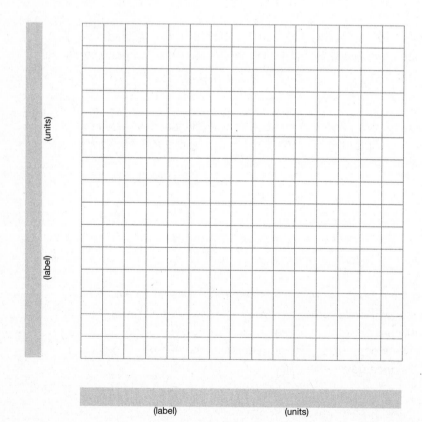

(units)

(label)

(label)   (units)

Assignment

Name _____ Date _____

Saving Money
Writing Equations of Lines

A marathon runner checks his watch at the halfway point (13 miles) of the Boston Marathon and sees that he has been running for about 100 minutes. He realizes that in order to match his personal best he will have to run faster. His personal best time for 26 miles is 191 minutes.

1. In this scenario, what are the two variable quantities? Let the time in minutes be the dependent variable and let the distance in miles be the independent variable. Use a complete sentence in your answer.

2. Identify the two points given in the problem statement.

3. What is the runner's rate (slope) during the second half of the race in minutes per mile? Show all your work and use a complete sentence in your answer.

4. Write an equation in slope-intercept form that gives the time in terms of the distance. Use x to represent the distance in miles and y to represent the time in minutes. Show all your work.

Find an equation of the line that passes through each given set of points. Write your equation in slope-intercept form. Show all your work.

5. (1, 2) and (2, 0)

6. (4, 100) and (6, 200)

5

Assignment

Name _____ Date _____

Spending Money
Linear and Piecewise Functions

1. Explain the difference between a linear function and a piecewise function. Use complete sentences in your answer.

The college library pays its student workers every 2 weeks. On payday, one of the workers receives a $270 check for the hours that he spends shelving books. The first week (7 days) after payday the student generally does the majority of his shopping and spends an average of about $25 per day. The next 5 days he spends an average of $15 per day, and the last 2 days before the next payday he spends only $10 per day.

2. Complete the table below that shows the amount of money left after different numbers of days.

Time since payday	Money left
days	dollars
0	
1	
2	
3	
4	
5	
6	
7	
8	
9	
10	
11	
12	
13	
14	

3. Create a graph from the table to show the relationship between the time since payday and the amount of money left. First, choose your bounds and intervals. Be sure to label your graph clearly.

Variable quantity	Lower bound	Upper bound	Interval
Time since payday			
Money left			

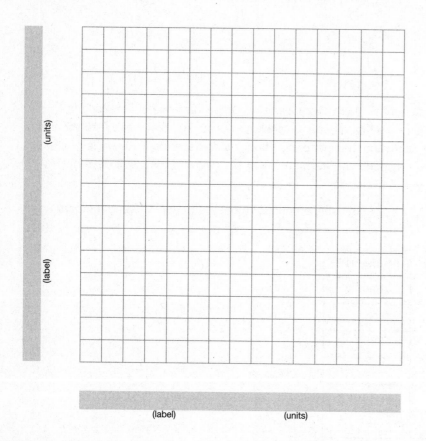

(units)

(label)

(label)   (units)

4. Write a piecewise function *f* for the graph in Question 3. Use *x* to represent a number from the domain of your function *f*.

5. Does the domain of the function *f* accurately represent the domain when you consider the problem situation? Use complete sentences in your answer.

5

Assignment

Name _____ Date _____

The School Play
Standard Form of a Linear Equation

The athletic department will raise money by charging admission to an upcoming football game. The price will be different for students and adults. Student tickets cost $3 each and adult tickets cost $5 each.

1. Write an expression that represents the total amount of money the athletic department will raise from the sale of x student tickets and y adult tickets.

2. The goal is to raise $5000 from the sale of tickets to the game. Write an equation that can be used to find the number of student and adult tickets sold if the goal is reached.

3. Using the equation from Question 2, write the intercepts of the equation's graph. Show all your work.

4. What do the intercepts mean in terms of the problem situation? Use complete sentences in your answer.

5. Create a graph of the equation in Question 2 to show the relationship between student tickets and adult tickets. First, choose your bounds and intervals. Be sure to label your graph clearly.

Variable quantity	Lower bound	Upper bound	Interval
Student tickets			
Adult tickets			

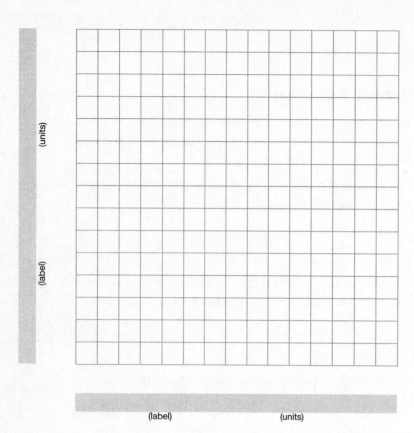

(units)

(label)

(label)   (units)

6. Assuming the athletic department met its goal of $5000, find the number of student tickets sold if 600 adult tickets sold. Use complete sentences to explain your reasoning.

7. Assuming the athletic department met its goal of $5000, find the number of adult tickets sold if 400 student tickets sold. Use complete sentences to explain your reasoning.

8. Write the equation in Question 2 in slope-intercept form. Show all your work.

5

Assignment

Name _____ Date _____

Earning Interest
Solving Literal Equations

1. A formula for the area of a rectangle is $A = bh$, where b is the length of the base of the rectangle and h is the height of the rectangle. Solve the equation for h. Show all your work. Then use a complete sentence to explain how you can find the height when you know the area and length of the base.

2. The formula for the area of a triangle is $A = \frac{1}{2}bh$, where b is the length of the base of the triangle and h is the height of the triangle. Solve the equation for b. Show all your work. Then use a complete sentence to explain how you can find the length of the base when you know the area and the height.

3. The formula for the diameter of a circle is $d = 2r$, where r is the radius of the circle. Solve the equation for r. Show all your work. Then use a complete sentence to explain how you can find the radius when you know the diameter.

4. The formula for the perimeter of a rectangle is $P = 2l + 2w$, where l is the length of the rectangle and w is the width of the rectangle. Solve the equation for w. Show all your work.

5

Assignment

Assignment for Lesson 6.1

Name _____   Date _____

Mia's Growing Like a Weed
Drawing the Line of Best Fit

The typical gestational period (time from conception to birth) for a human baby is about 40 weeks. Recent developments in ultrasound scanning allow doctors to make measurements of parts of a baby's body while it is still in the womb. The table below contains data about the length of a baby's femur (thigh bone) during gestation.

Gestation time	Femur length
weeks	centimeters
14	1.5
14.5	1.6
15	2.0
16	2.1
20	3.3
25	4.8
30	6.2
40	8.0

1. Write unit rates that compare the baby's change in femur length to the change in gestation time from 14 weeks to 14.5 weeks, from 16 weeks to 20 weeks, and from 30 weeks to 40 weeks. Show all your work.

2. Do all the data points lie on the same line? What does this tell you about the baby's femur length change over time? Use complete sentences to explain your reasoning.

© 2008 Carnegie Learning, Inc.

Chapter 6 ■ Assignments   87

3. Write ordered pairs from the table that show the baby's femur length as a function of gestation time.

4. Create a scatter plot of the ordered pairs in Question 3 to show the relationship between gestation time and femur length. First, choose your bounds and intervals. Be sure to label your graph clearly.

Variable quantity	Lower bound	Upper bound	Interval
Gestation time			
Femur length			

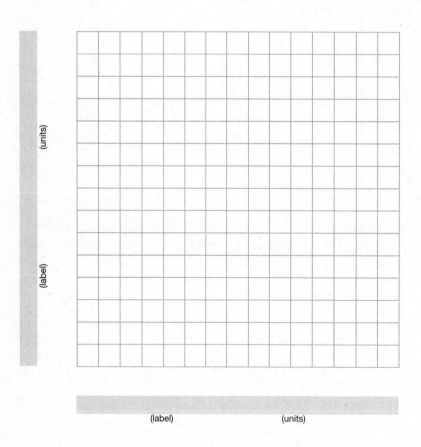

(units)

(label)

(label)   (units)

5. Use a ruler to draw the line that best fits your data in your graph in Question 4. Then write the equation of your line. Be sure to define your variables and include the units.

6

6. According to your line, approximately how many centimeters did the femur grow each week from 14 weeks to 40 weeks? How did you find your answer? Use complete sentences in your answer.

7. According to your line, approximately how long would the baby's femur have been when the gestation time is 7 weeks? Show all your work and use a complete sentence in your answer.

8. According to your line, approximately how long would the baby's femur have been when the gestation time is 8 weeks? Show all your work and use a complete sentence in your answer.

9. Do your answers to Questions 7 and 8 make sense? Use complete sentences in your answer.

10. What can you conclude about the accuracy of your model? Use a complete sentence in your answer.

6

Assignment

Name _____ Date _____

Where Do You Buy Your Music?
Using Lines of Best Fit

The table below shows the percent of voter participation in U.S. presidential elections for the years 1956 to 2000.

Election year	Voter participation
year	percent
1956	59.3
1960	62.8
1964	61.9
1968	60.9
1972	55.2
1976	53.5
1980	54.0
1984	53.1
1988	50.2
1992	55.9
1996	49.0
2000	50.7

1. Because the x-coordinates represent time, we can define time as the number of years since 1956. So, 1956 would become 0. What number would you use for 1960? What number would you use for 1964? What number would you use for 1968? Use complete sentences to explain your reasoning.

2. Write the ordered pairs that show the percent of voter participation as a function of the number of years since 1956.

3. Looking at the data, do you think your line of best fit will have a positive slope or a negative slope? Use a complete sentence to explain your reasoning.

6

4. Create a scatter plot of the ordered pairs in Question 2 to show the relationship between time and voter participation. First, choose your bounds and intervals. Be sure to label your graph clearly.

Variable quantity	Lower bound	Upper bound	Interval
Time			
Voter participation			

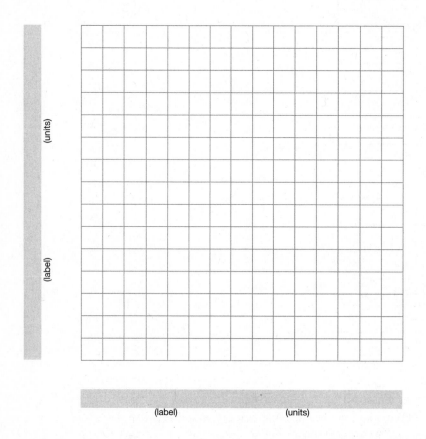

(units)

(label)

(label)   (units)

5. Use a ruler to ruler to draw the line that best fits the data in the graph. Then write the equation of the line. Be sure to define your variables and include the units.

6. Use your equation to predict the percent of voter participation in 2008. Show all your work and use a complete sentence in your answer.

6

© 2008 Carnegie Learning, Inc.

7. Considering the problem situation, what is the domain of your function? Use a complete sentence to explain your reasoning.

8. Use your equation to predict the year in which the voter participation will be 45%. Show all your work and use a complete sentence in your answer.

9. Use your equation to determine what the voter participation was in 1980. Show all your work and use a complete sentence in your answer.

10. How close is your answer to Question 9 to the actual data? Use a complete sentence in your answer.

11. Consider a line of best fit for the percent of non-voters over time. Would this line increase or decrease from left to right? How would the line's steepness compare to the steepness of the line in Question 4? Use complete sentences in your answer.

6

Assignment

Name _____ Date _____

Stroop Test
Performing an Experiment

The goal of a word recall experiment is to see how many words from a list that is read aloud that a person can memorize and repeat back. Five word lists are given below.

5-Word List: chair, shoe, horse, suitcase, lamp

7-Word List: animal, sweater, cheetah, avocado, back, desk, plant

10-Word List: stereo, basketball, violin, teacher, pear, baby, table, zoo, curtains, ox

15-Word List: cup, barn, paper, book, fire, comb, glass, vacuum, cloud, road, suit, stereo, computer, trunk, television

20-Word List: football, hair, pizza, scarf, sandwich, T-shirt, microphone, screen, clock, fingers, coat, watch, tires, candles, cushions, earrings, heater, picture, keyboard, soda

1. If you were to perform a word recall experiment, what results would you expect to see as the number of words increases? Do you expect people to remember more words or fewer words? Do you think people will remember the same percent of words as the length of the list increases? Use complete sentences in your answer.

2. What are the two variable quantities in a word recall experiment? Which variable quantity depends on the other? Use complete sentences in your answer.

3. Perform the experiment for each word list. Read each list of words slowly and clearly to someone, but do not repeat any of the words. After you have finished reading each list, the person should repeat any words he or she remembers back to you. Do not allow the person to write anything down. Keep track of how many words the person correctly repeats back to you by filling in the table on the next page. Repeat this experiment two more times and average the results.

List length (words)	Trial 1 (words recalled)	Trial 2 (words recalled)	Trial 3 (words recalled)	Average (words recalled)
5-word list				
7-word list				
10-word list				
15-word list				
20-word list				

4. Write the ordered pairs from the from the table that show the average number of words recalled as a function of the number of words in the list.

5. Create a scatter plot of the ordered pairs in Question 4 to show the relationship between list length and words recalled. First, choose your bounds and intervals. Be sure to label your graph clearly.

Variable quantity	Lower bound	Upper bound	Interval
List length			
Words recalled			

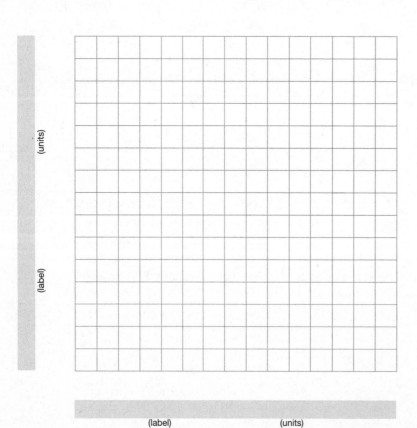

(units)

(label)

(label)   (units)

6. Use a ruler to draw a line of best fit. Then write the equation of your line.

7. Find the *y*-intercept of your line. What does the *y*-intercept represent in this situation? Use complete sentences in your answer.

8. Find the slope of your line. What does the slope represent in this situation? Use complete sentences in your answer.

9. What is the average number of words that should be recalled from a list of 25 words? What is the average number of words that should be recalled from a list of 35 words? What is the average number of words that should be recalled from a list of 50 words? Show all your work and use complete sentences in your answer.

10. What length should the word list be if a person recalls 20 words? Show your work and use a complete sentence in your answer.

6

6

Assignment

Name _____ Date _____

Jumping
Correlation

Define each term in your own words.

1. correlation

2. positive correlation

3. negative correlation

Decide whether each set of data most likely has a positive correlation, a negative correlation, or no correlation. Use a complete sentence in your answer.

4. The number of hours you study compared to your test score

5. Your running speed compared to the time that it takes you to run the 100-meter dash

6. The number of calories that you eat compared to your weight

7. The number of computers sold compared to the amount of rainfall in inches

8. Give examples of two variable quantities that are positively correlated, two variable quantities that are negatively correlated, and two variable quantities that are not correlated.

6

Assignment

Name _____ Date _____

Human Chain: Wrist Experiment
Using Technology to Find a Linear Regression Equation, Part 1

The table below shows the number of students per computer in U.S. public schools.

School year	Students per computer
year	students
1984	125
1985	75
1986	50
1987	37
1988	32
1989	25
1990	22
1991	20
1992	18
1993	16
1994	14
1995	10.5
1996	10
1997	7.8
1998	6.1
1999	5.7
2000	5.4

1. Because the *x*-coordinates represent time, we can define time as the number of years since 1984. So, 1984 would become 0. What number would you use for 1990? What number would you use for 1996? What number would you use for 2000? Use complete sentences to explain your reasoning.

2. Write the ordered pairs that show the number of students per computer as a function of the number of years since 1984.

3. Use a graphing calculator to find the linear regression equation. Round the values of the slope and the y-intercept to the nearest hundredth.

4. What is the value of r for your linear regression equation? Does this indicate a positive or negative correlation? Use a complete sentence in your answer.

5. What is the slope of your linear regression equation? What does the slope mean in this problem situation? Use a complete sentence in your answer.

6. What is the y-intercept of your linear regression equation? What does the y-intercept mean in this problem situation? Use a complete sentence in your answer.

7. How does the y-intercept of your linear regression equation compare to the actual data? Use complete sentences in your answer.

8. Is your linear regression equation a good model of the data? Show all your work and use complete sentences in your answer.

© 2008 Carnegie Learning, Inc.

Assignment

Name _____ Date _____

Human Chain: Shoulder Experiment
Using Technology to Find a Linear Regression Equation, Part 2

The table below shows the yearly cost of tuition at a private four-year college.

School year	Cost of tuition
year	dollars
1993	10,294
1994	10,952
1995	11,481
1996	12,243
1997	12,881
1998	13,344
1999	13,973
2000	14,588
2001	15,531

1. Because the x-coordinates represent time, we can define time as the number of years since 1993. So, 1993 would become 0. What number would you use for 2000? Use a complete sentence in your answer.

2. Write the ordered pairs that show the yearly tuition cost as a function of the number of years since 1993.

6

3. Use a graphing calculator to find the linear regression equation. Round the values of the slope and y-intercept to the nearest dollar.

4. Why is it more appropriate to round the slope and y-intercept of the linear regression equation in Question 3 to nearest dollar instead of to the nearest cent? Use complete sentences in your answer.

5. What is the value of r for your linear regression equation? Does this indicate a positive or negative correlation? Use a complete sentence in your answer.

6. What is the slope of your linear regression equation? What does the slope mean in this problem situation? Use a complete sentence in your answer.

7. Use your linear regression equation to predict the cost of tuition in 2005. Show all your work and use a complete sentence in your answer.

8. Use your linear regression equation to determine in which year the cost of tuition will be $25,000. Show all your work and use a complete sentence in your answer.

6

Assignment

Name _____ Date _____

Making a Quilt
Scatter Plots and Non-Linear Data

An automatic sprinkler system includes ground-level sprinkler heads that rotate to water a circular area. The radius of the circular area can be adjusted at installation to accommodate the shape of any yard.

1. Complete the table below that shows the watering area for different sprinkling radii. Recall that the area of a circle is $A = \pi r^2$, where $\pi \approx 3.14$.

Radius	Area
feet	square feet
0	
1	
2	
3	
4	
5	
6	
7	

2. Write the ordered pairs that show the area as a function of the watering radius.

3. Create a scatter plot of the ordered pairs on the grid to show the relationship between radius and area. First, choose your bounds and intervals. Be sure to label your graph clearly.

Variable quantity	Lower bound	Upper bound	Interval
Radius			
Area			

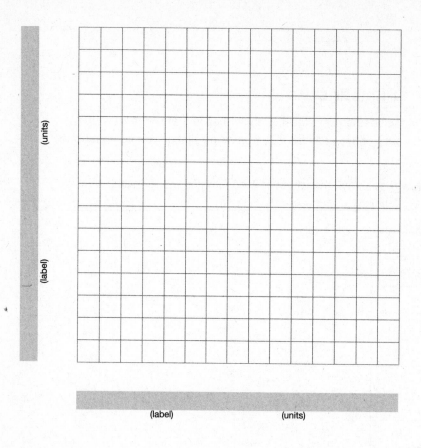

4. Use a graphing calculator to find the linear regression equation.

5. Find the watering area when the sprinkler radius is 10 feet as you did when you filled in the chart in Question 1. Then use the equation in Question 4 to find the area. What can you conclude about your linear model? Use complete sentences in your answer.

6

Name _____ Date _____

Making and Selling Markers and T-Shirts
Using a Graph to Solve a Linear System

1. Define break-even point in your own words.

2. How can a graph be used to determine the break-even point? Use a complete sentence in your answer.

A company makes and sells flags with various seasonal themes. It costs $12 to manufacture each flag, and there is a set-up cost of $200 for a new design. The company sells the flags to home improvement stores for $20 per flag.

3. Write an equation for the production cost in dollars in terms of the number of flags produced. Be sure to describe what your variables represent. Use a complete sentence in your answer.

4. Write an equation for the income in dollars in terms of the number of flags sold. Be sure to describe what your variables represent. Use a complete sentence in your answer.

5. Complete the table of values that shows the production cost and income for different numbers of flags with the same design.

Quantity Name	Number of flags	Production cost	Income
Unit	flags	dollars	dollars
Expression	x		
	0		
	20		
	30		
	50		
	120		

6. Create a graph of both the production cost and income equations on the grid below. Use the bounds and intervals below. Be sure to label your graph clearly.

Variable quantity	Lower bound	Upper bound	Interval
Flags	0	150	10
Money	0	3000	200

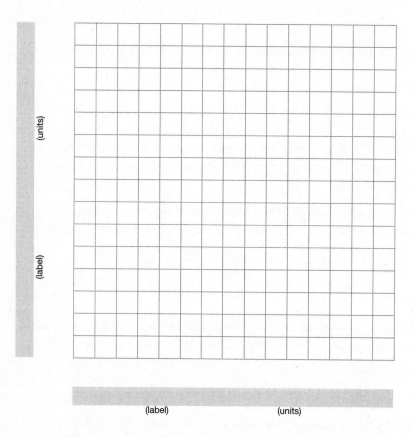

(units)

(label)

(label)   (units)

7. What is the break-even point for making and selling flags? Use a complete sentence in your answer.

8. What is the company's profit at the break-even point? Show all your work and use a complete sentence in your answer.

Assignment

Name _____ Date _____

Time Study
Graphs and Solutions of Linear Systems

1. Describe the graph of a linear system with one solution, a linear system with no solutions, and a linear system with infinitely many solutions. Use complete sentences in your answer.

Two window washers are cleaning the windows of a skyscraper. By 11:00 A.M., the first window washer, Wally, has already cleaned 12 windows and cleans at a rate of 4 windows per hour. Wally's partner, Wanda, started work late today. She has only washed 8 windows by 11:00 A.M., but she cleans at a rate of 5 windows per hour.

2. For each worker, write an equation that gives the total number of windows washed y in terms of the time worked x in hours since 11:00 A.M.

3. Complete the table of values that shows the number of windows washed by Wally and Wanda for different numbers of hours worked.

Quantity Name	Time worked since 11:00 A.M.	Windows washed by Wally	Windows washed by Wanda
Unit	hours	windows	windows
Expression	x		
	0		
	2		
	5		
	8		
	10		

4. Write a linear system that shows the total number of windows washed in terms of the time worked since 11:00 A.M. for both washers.

5. Does the linear system in Question 4 have one solution, no solution, or infinitely many solutions? Use complete sentences to justify your answer.

6. Based on the values in the table in Question 3, estimate when Wally and Wanda will have washed the same number of windows. Use complete sentences to justify your estimate.

7. Create a graph of the linear system on the grid below. First, choose your bounds and intervals. Be sure to label your graph clearly.

Variable quantity	Lower bound	Upper bound	Interval
Time worked since 11:00 A.M.			
Windows			

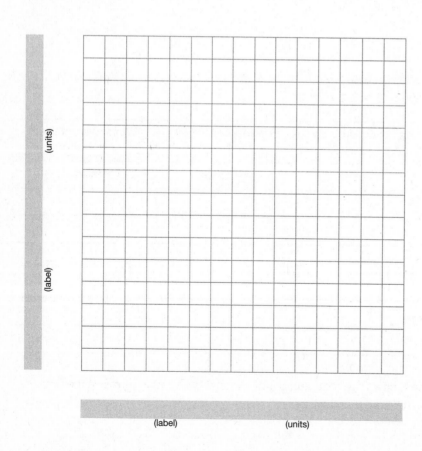

(units)

(label)

(label)　　　(units)

8. What is the solution of the linear system in this problem situation? Use a complete sentence in your answer.

9. Algebraically verify that the ordered pair in Question 8 is the solution to the system.

10. What does the solution mean in context of this problem situation? Use a complete sentence in your answer.

Determine whether the graphs of each pair of equations are parallel, perpendicular, or neither. Show all your work and use a complete sentence to explain your reasoning.

11. $y = 2x - 5$ and $y = -2x + 4$

12. $y = 3x + 6$ and $y = -3(-1 - x)$

13. $y = 0.2x + 9$ and $y = -5x - 7$

Assignment

Name _____ Date _____

Hiking Trip
Using Substitution to Solve a Linear System

The school dance team raised money by charging admission to the spring ballet. They charged $2 for each student ticket and $5 for each adult ticket, raising $510 from ticket sales.

1. Write an equation in standard form that relates the numbers of adult tickets and student tickets bought for $510. Let x represent the number of student tickets bought and let y represent the number of adult tickets bought.

2. Adults bought 3 times the number of tickets that students bought. Write an equation in x and y as defined in Question 1 that represents this situation.

3. Do 50 student tickets and 100 adult tickets satisfy the equations in Questions 1 and 2? Show all your work.

4. Use the substitution method to solve the linear system. Show all your work.

5. What does the solution in Question 4 mean in context of the problem situation? Use a complete sentence in your answer.

Solve each linear system by using the substitution method. Show all your work and use a complete sentence in your answer. Then check your answer algebraically.

6. $y = 2x$

    $3x + 2y = 21$

7. $5x + 4y = 110$

    $y = 1.5x$

8. $3x - 2y = 24$

    $x = 2y$

9. $5x - 3y = 23$

    $x + y = 3$

Assignment

Name _____ Date _____

Basketball Tournament
Using Linear Combinations to Solve a Linear System

Cafeteria workers at a summer camp are preparing lunches for all the campers and counselors. The total number of campers and counselors is 300. The difference between the number of campers and the number of counselors is 280.

1. Write an equation in standard form that represents the total number of people at the camp. Let x represent the number of campers and let y represent the number of counselors.

2. Write an equation in standard form that represents the difference between the numbers of campers and counselors.

3. Write the linear system for this problem situation below.

4. Solve the linear system in Question 3. Show all your work and write your answer in a complete sentence.

5. Check your solution algebraically. Show all your work.

6. Check your solution by creating a graph of your linear system on the grid below. First, choose your bounds and intervals. Be sure to label your graph clearly.

Variable quantity	Lower bound	Upper bound	Interval
Campers			
Counselors			

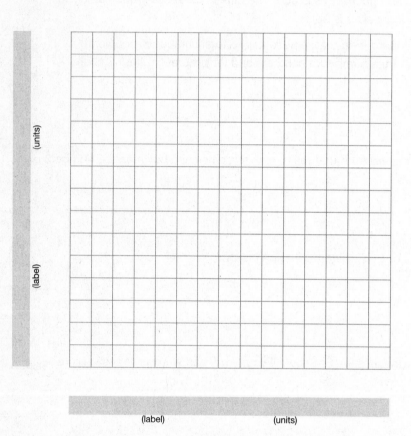

(units)

(label)

(label)   (units)

7. For the linear system below, describe two different first steps you could take to solve the system by using the linear combination method. Identify the variable that will be solved for when you add equations for each case. Use complete sentences in your answer.

$-4x + 5y = 20$

$2x - 10y = 20$

Assignment

Name _____ Date _____

Finding the Better Paying Job
Using the Best Method to Solve a Linear System, Part 1

You are offered two different summer jobs and you need to decide which one will pay the most money. The first job, a camp counselor position, pays $200 up front plus $7 per hour. The second job, a cashier position at a sporting goods store, pays $10 per hour.

1. Write an equation that gives the total earnings from the counselor position in dollars in terms of the time worked in hours. Be sure to define your variables. Use a complete sentence in your answer.

2. Write an equation that gives the total earnings from the cashier position in dollars in terms of the time worked in hours. Be sure to define your variables. Use a complete sentence in your answer.

3. Use an algebraic method to determine whether the total earnings from the counselor position will ever be the same as the total earnings from the cashier position. Show all your work and use a complete sentence in your answer.

4. If the total earnings will be the same, what will the total earnings be? Show all your work and use a complete sentence in your answer.

5. Which method did you use to find the answer to Question 3? Use a complete sentence to explain your choice.

6. Check your solution by creating a graph of your linear system on the grid below. First, choose your bounds and intervals. Be sure to label your graph clearly.

Variable quantity	Lower bound	Upper bound	Interval
Time worked			
Total earnings			

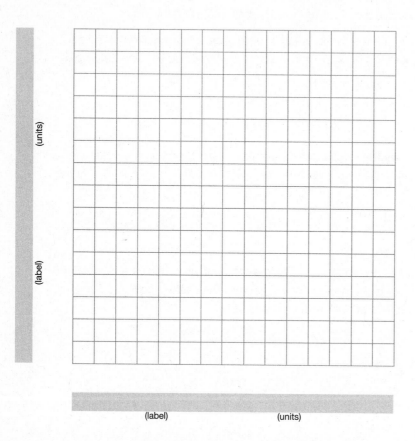

(units)

(label)

(label)   (units)

7. Write a short paragraph explaining which job is the better choice. Use the information from the linear system and the graph to support your decision.

Assignment

Name _____ Date _____

World Oil: Supply and Demand
Using the Best Method to Solve a Linear System, Part 2

The weather report just announced that a huge winter storm is coming to the area. Local residents are concerned that they will be confined to their houses, so they begin stocking up on groceries and drinking water. The local grocery store currently has 500 gallons of drinking water, and they have placed orders so that 50 gallons of water are shipped to the store every hour. The grocery store manager has calculated that anxious residents are purchasing water at a rate of 71 gallons per hour.

1. Write an equation that gives the grocery store's supply of water in terms of the time in hours. Be sure to define your variables.

2. Write an expression for the demand for water in gallons in terms of the time in hours. Be sure to define your variables.

3. Complete the table of values below that shows the supply and demand.

Quantity Name	Time	Supply	Demand
Unit	hours	gallons	gallons
Expression	x		
	0		
	5		
	10		
	15		
	20		
	25		
	30		

4. Based on the table in Question 3, estimate when the store will run out of drinking water. Use a complete sentence to explain your reasoning.

5. Solve a system of equations to determine when the store will run out of drinking water. Show all your work and use a complete sentence in your answer.

6. Check your answers to Questions 4 and 5 by creating a graph of your linear system on the grid below. First, choose your bounds and intervals. Be sure to label your graph clearly.

Variable quantity	Lower bound	Upper bound	Interval
Time			
Water			

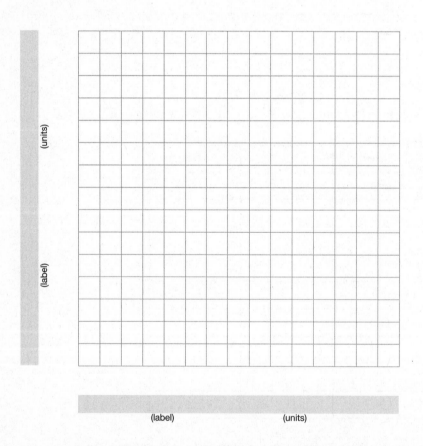

(units)

(label)

(label)   (units)

7. You have just used three different methods to determine the point of intersection of a linear system. What are the three methods?

Assignment

Name _____ Date _____

Picking the Better Option
Solving Linear Systems

Two proposals are being considered for the redevelopment of an old building. The first proposal is to turn the building into a few large, deluxe apartments. The cost of redevelopment is $500,000 and the maintenance is expected to cost $1000 per month. The second proposal is to convert the building into many small apartments. This redevelopment will be less expensive, at a cost of only $250,000, but maintenance is expected to cost $2500 per month.

1. For each plan, write an equation that gives the total expenses in dollars in terms of the time in months. Be sure to define your variables.

2. For each plan, what do the slope and *y*-intercept of the graph of the equation represent in the problem situation? Use complete sentences in your answer.

3. Will there be a number of months for which the total expenses are the same? How do you know? Use a complete sentence to explain your reasoning.

4. Describe the different methods you can use to find the number of months for which the total expenses are the same. Use a complete sentence in your answer.

5. Use an algebraic method to find the number of months for which the total expenses are the same. Then describe the numbers of months for which each plan is the least expensive.

6. Now consider the income that the apartments are expected to generate. The developers expect to make $7500 each month from renting the apartments. Write an equation that gives the total earnings in dollars in terms of the number of months the apartments are rented.

7. For each plan, determine the break-even point. Show all your work and use complete sentences in your answer.

8. Use the results from Question 7 to describe the number of months for which each plan is better. Use complete sentences in your answer.

Assignment

Name _____ Date _____

Video Arcade
Writing and Graphing an Inequality in Two Variables

The senior class plans to raise money to help pay for a local playground. The class sets a goal to raise at least $2000 by washing cars and selling T-shirts. Every car washed earns $5 and every T-shirt sold earns $8.

1. If the class washes 100 cars and sells 150 T-shirts, will the goal be reached?
   Show your work.

2. If the class washes 150 cars and sells 200 T-shirts, will the goal be reached?
   Show your work.

3. Write an expression that represents the total money raised. Let x represent the number of cars washed and let y represent the number of T-shirts sold.

4. Complete the table that shows the total money raised for different numbers of cars washed and T-shirts sold.

Quantity Name	Cars washed	T-shirts sold	Money raised
Unit	cars	T-shirts	dollars
	0	250	
	25	175	
	50	150	
	200	200	
	125	200	
	200	125	

5. Which ordered pairs from the table in Question 4 satisfy the problem situation?

6. Write an equation that represents the number of cars washed x and the number of T-shirts sold y that raises exactly $2000.

7. Find the *x*- and *y*-intercepts of your equation in Question 6.

8. Use the intercepts to graph the equation in Question 6 on the grid below. Use the bounds and intervals given below. Be sure to label your graph clearly.

Variable quantity	Lower bound	Upper bound	Interval
Number of cars washed			
Number of shirts sold			

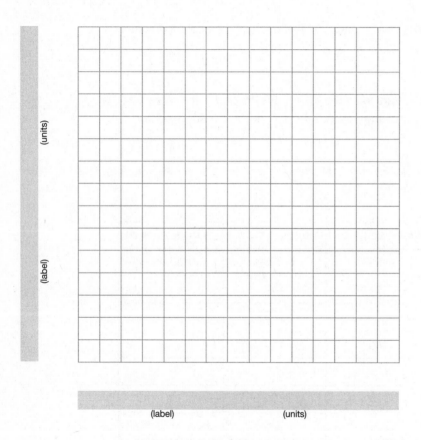

(units)

(label)

(label)   (units)

9. Write a linear inequality that represents the number of cars washed *x* and the number of T-shirts sold *y* that raises at least $2000.

10. Plot the ordered pairs from Question 5 on the grid above.

11. Shade the region on the graph above that shows all the points that satisfy the inequality in Question 9.

© 2008 Carnegie Learning, Inc.

Assignment

Name _____   Date _____

Making a Mosaic
Solving Systems of Linear Inequalities

Solve each system of linear inequalities by filling in the missing information for each inequality and then graphing.

1. $3x + 3y \geq -18$

　　$x + 2y < 4$

　　$3x + 3y \geq -18$　　x-intercept: _____

　　　　　　　　　　　　y-intercept: _____

　　　　　　　　　　　　Solid or dashed line? _____

　　　　　　　　　　　　Test (0, 0): _____

　　　　　　　　　　　　_____

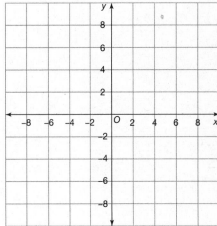

　　$x + 2y < 4$　　　　x-intercept: _____

　　　　　　　　　　　　y-intercept: _____

　　　　　　　　　　　　Solid or dashed line? _____

　　　　　　　　　　　　Test (0, 0): _____

　　　　　　　　　　　　_____

2. $4x + 8y < 32$

　　$y - x > 3$

　　$4x + 8y < 32$　　x-intercept: _____

　　　　　　　　　　　　y-intercept: _____

　　　　　　　　　　　　Solid or dashed line? _____

　　　　　　　　　　　　Test (0, 0): _____

　　　　　　　　　　　　_____

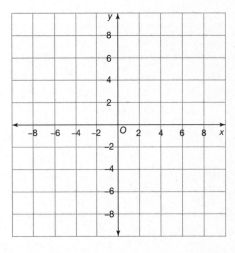

　　$y - x > 3$　　　　x-intercept: _____

　　　　　　　　　　　　y-intercept: _____

　　　　　　　　　　　　Solid or dashed line? _____

　　　　　　　　　　　　Test (0, 0): _____

　　　　　　　　　　　　_____

7

Assignment

Name _____ Date _____

Website Design
Introduction to Quadratic Functions

Identify the values of *a*, *b*, and *c* in each quadratic function.

1. $y = 2x^2 + 3x - 1$ **2.** $y = 3x^2 - 5x$ **3.** $y = x^2 + 4x + 2$

Evaluate each quadratic function for the given value of *x*. Show all your work.

4. $f(x) = 2x^2 + 3x - 1; f(2)$ **5.** $f(x) = 3x^2 - 5x; f(-1)$ **6.** $f(x) = x^2 + 4x; f(0)$

As the set designer for your school play, you have to build an archway for one of the scenes. The archway needs to be 14 feet wide and 12 feet high. Before cutting the archway in a piece of plywood, you draw a plan on a coordinate grid. The table below shows some of the points of the archway with respect to the origin. The origin represents the lower left-hand corner of the plywood sheet where you will begin cutting.

Quantity Name	Horizontal distance	Vertical distance
Unit	feet	feet
	0	0
	5	11.02
	7	12
	9	11.02
	14	0

7. Create a scatter plot of the points of the archway on the grid. First, choose your bounds and intervals. Be sure to label your graph clearly.

Variable quantity	Lower bound	Upper bound	Interval

(units)

(label)

(label)   (units)

8. Connect the points with a smooth curve to create the drawing of the archway.

Assignment

Name _____ Date _____

Satellite Dish
Parabolas

Define each term in your own words.

1. parabola

2. vertex

3. axis of symmetry

For each function, algebraically determine the vertex and the axis of symmetry of the graph. Then draw the graph for each function. Identify the domain and range for each function.

4. $y = x^2 + 3$

5. $y = -x^2 + 3x + 5$

Assignment

Name _____ Date _____

Dog Run
Comparing Linear and Quadratic Functions

1. What is the formula for the area of a square A with side length x?

2. Based on Lesson 8.3, what effect do you think doubling the side length of a square has on its area? Use a complete sentence in your answer.

3. Complete the table below to show different side lengths and areas of a square.

Side length	Area
cm	sq cm
1	
3	
9	
27	
81	

4. Create a graph that shows the area as a function of the side length on the grid. First, choose your bounds and intervals. Be sure to label your graph clearly.

Variable quantity	Lower bound	Upper bound	Interval

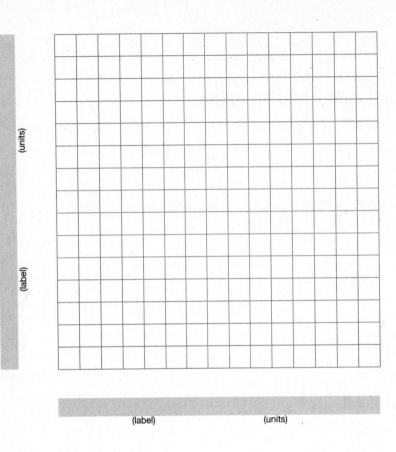

(units)

(label)

(label)   (units)

5. Describe the rate of change of the side length in the table in Question 3.

6. Based on Questions 3 and 4, what effect do you think tripling the side length of a square has on its area? Use a complete sentence in your answer.

7. What effect do you think halving the side length of a square has on its area? Use a complete sentence in your answer.

Assignment

Name _____ Date _____

Guitar Strings and Other Things
Square Roots and Radicals

The principal of a local elementary school is hiring contractors to design and build a new playground. The playground will consist of several small play areas with grass in between. The small play areas will be built with a rubber base instead of concrete.

1. The swings will be built on a square rubber base. Let s represent the side length in feet and A represent the area in square feet. What is the area of the rubber base if the side length is 10 feet? What is the area of the rubber base if the side length is 15 feet? What is the area of the rubber base if the side length is 20 feet? Show all your work and use complete sentences in your answer.

2. What is the side length of the square rubber base if its area is 144 square feet? What is the side length of the square rubber base if its area is 196 square feet? What is the side length of the square rubber base if its area is 625 square feet? Show all your work and use complete sentences in your answer.

3. The slide will be built on a circular rubber base. Let r represent the radius in feet and A represent the area in square feet. What is the area of the circular rubber base if the radius is 4 feet? What is the area of the circular rubber base if the radius is 6 feet? What is the area of the circular rubber base if the radius is 10 feet? The formula for the area of a circle is $A = 3.14r^2$. Show all your work and use complete sentences in your answer.

4. What is the radius of the circular rubber base if its area is 100 square feet?
What is the radius of the circular rubber base if its area is 200 square feet?
What is the radius of the circular rubber base if its area is 300 square feet?
What is the radius of the circular rubber base if its area is A square feet?
Show all your work and use complete sentences in your answer.

5. Equations that have a variable to the second power generally have two solutions. Does this make sense in this problem situation? Why or why not? Use a complete sentence in your answer.

Identify which point on the number line below matches each value.

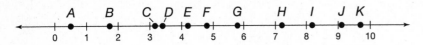

6. $\sqrt{10}$ **7.** $\sqrt{83}$ **8.** $\sqrt{52}$

9. $\sqrt{23}$ **10.** $\sqrt{67}$ **11.** $\sqrt{3}$

Assignment

Name _____ Date _____

Tent Designing Competition
Solving by Factoring and Extracting Square Roots

A manufacturing company just received a contract to make different-sized cones that will be used by the state Department of Transportation. The formula for volume of a cone will be used in their planning and manufacturing of the product. The formula is $V = \frac{1}{3}\pi r^2 h$, where r is the radius of the base of the cone and h is the height.

1. What is the volume of the cone when the radius is 0.5 foot and the height is 2 feet? What is the volume of the cone when the radius is 0.75 feet and the height is 2.5 feet? Use 3.14 for π. Show all your work and use complete sentences in your answer.

2. One cone has a volume of 1 cubic foot and a height of 2 feet. Write an equation that you can use to find the radius of the cone.

3. Get the variable by itself on one side of the equation from Question 2 and simplify. Use 3.14 for π and show all your work.

4. Use a calculator to approximate the solutions of the equation in Question 3 to the nearest tenth.

5. What is the radius of the cone? Use a complete sentence in your answer.

For each quadratic function below, find the *x*-intercepts, the *y*-intercept, and sketch its graph. Show all your work.

6. $y = \dfrac{1}{4}(x + 4)(x - 4)$

  x-intercepts: _____

  y-intercept: _____

7. $y = -2(x - 2)(x + 2)$

  x-intercepts: _____

  y-intercept: _____

Assignment

Name _____ Date _____

Kicking a Soccer Ball
Using the Quadratic Formula to Solve Quadratic Equations

Consider the quadratic function $y = x^2 + 2x - 3$ for Questions 1 through 5.

1. Complete the table of values below and then sketch the graph.

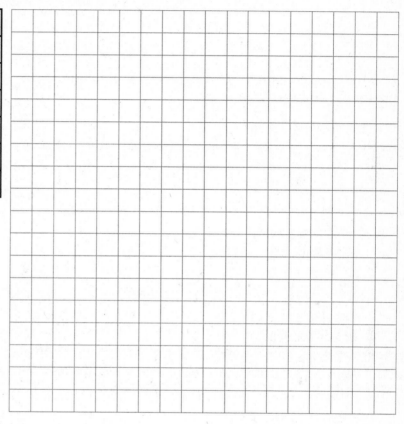

x	y
−2	
−1	
0	
1	
2	
3	

2. Using the table and graph, identify the x-intercepts.

3. Write an equation that you can use to algebraically find the x-intercepts.

4. For the equation in Question 3, find the values of *a*, *b*, and *c*. Then solve the equation using the quadratic formula. Show all your work.

Use the discriminant to write a quadratic equation for each given number of solutions. Show all your work.

5. no real solutions

6. one rational solution

7. two real solutions

8. Which method for solving quadratic equations can be used to solve any quadratic equation? Use complete sentences in your answer.

Assignment

Name _____ Date _____

Pumpkin Catapult
Using a Vertical Motion Model

A baseball player hits a foul ball straight up in the air from a height of 4 feet off the ground. The initial velocity as the ball comes off the bat is 130 feet per second. The motion of ball can be modeled by $y = -16t^2 + vt + h$, where t is the time in seconds, v is the initial velocity in feet per second, and h is the height off the ground in feet.

1. Write a quadratic function that models the height of the ball in terms of time.

2. What is the height of the ball after 1 second? What is the height of the ball after 2 seconds? What is the height of the ball after 10 seconds? Show all your work and use complete sentences in your answer.

3. Do all of the answers to Question 2 make sense? Use complete sentences in your answer.

4. Write an equation that you can use to find when the ball is 250 feet off the ground. Then solve the equation. Show all your work.

5. Do both solutions make sense? Use a complete sentence to in your answer.

6. When is the ball 250 feet above the ground? Use a complete sentence in your answer.

7. Write an equation that you can use to determine when the ball hits the ground. Then solve the equation. Show all your work.

8. Do both solutions have meaning in the problem situation? Use a complete sentence in your answer.

9. When does the ball hit the ground? Use a complete sentence in your answer.

10. When is the ball at its highest point? Show all your work and use a complete sentence in your answer.

11. What is the greatest height of the ball? Show all your work and use a complete sentence in your answer.

12. Complete the table of values that shows the height of the ball in terms of time.

Quantity Name	Time	Height
Unit	seconds	feet
Expression	t	
	0	
	2	
	4	
	6	
	8	
	10	

13. Create a graph of the model to see the path of the ball on the grid below and confirm your answers above. First, choose your bounds and intervals. Be sure to label your graph clearly.

Variable quantity	Lower bound	Upper bound	Interval

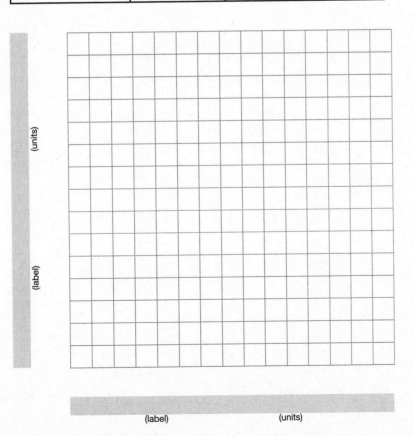

(units)

(label)

(label)   (units)

Assignment

Name _____ Date _____

Viewing the Night Sky
Using Quadratic Functions

Using the information from the scenario in Lesson 8.8, consider another telescope.
This telescope has an aperture of 6 inches and a focal length of 28 inches.

1. How does the telescope in this situation compare to the telescope in Problem 2 of
   Lesson 8.8? Use a complete sentence in your answer.

2. The height of the lens in Problem 2 of Lesson 8.8 is about 0.040. Predict the height of the
   lens in this situation. Use complete sentences in your answer.

3. Write the function that represents the lens shape.

4. Complete the table of values that shows the shape of the lens. Use the domain as a guide
   for choosing your x-values. If necessary, round your answers to the nearest thousandth.

Quantity Name	Horizontal position	Height
Unit	inches	inches
Expression		

5. What is the range of the function? Show all your work and use a complete sentence in your answer.

6. What is the maximum height of this lens? If necessary, round your answer to the nearest thousandth. Use a complete sentence to explain how you found your answer.

7. Create a graph of the quadratic function on the grid below. First, choose your bounds and intervals. Be sure to label to graph clearly.

Variable quantity	Lower bound	Upper bound	Interval

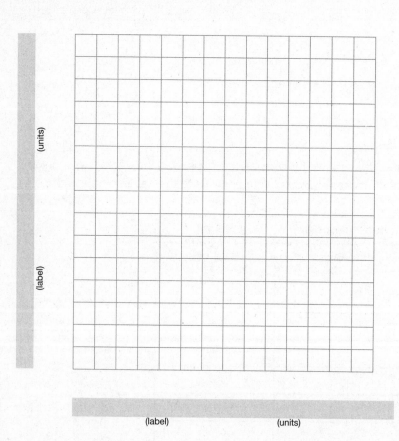

(units)

(label)

(label)   (units)

8. Did the table and graph verify your prediction in Question 2? Use a complete sentence in your answer.

Assignment

Name _____   Date _____

The Museum of Natural History
Powers and Prime Factorization

For each pair of numbers, list the common factors.

1. 18 and 56

2. 14 and 42

3. 19 and 81

The Washington Family Reunion is planning its annual softball tournament. The games are played for fun, but the organizers still want to make sure the teams are fair. Each team should have the same number of players, and each team should have the same number of adults. This year 12 adults and 54 children want to participate.

4. Can there be three teams competing in the softball tournament? Use complete sentences to explain your reasoning.

5. Can there be four teams competing in the softball tournament? Use complete sentences to explain your reasoning.

6. Can there be five teams competing in the softball tournament? Use complete sentences to explain your reasoning.

7. What are the different-sized teams that are possible for this number of adults and children? Describe the number of teams, and the number of adults and children on each team. Use complete sentences in your answer.

8. Which option from Question 7 is the best set-up for the softball tournament? Use complete sentences in your answer.

Assignment

Name _____ Date _____

Bits and Bytes
Multiplying and Dividing Powers

1. Can you use the rules you developed in Lesson 9.2 to simplify the expressions $6^3 \cdot 3^4$ and $\frac{7^6}{4^6}$? Why or why not? Use a complete sentence in your answer.

Your class is taking a trip to a large city. Your teacher tells you that the population of this city is 243 times greater than the population of your small town, which is 2187 people.

2. Find the population of the large city. Show all your work and use a complete sentence in your answer.

3. Write each factor in the product from Question 2 as a power of 3. Then use the rule from Lesson 9.2 to find the product. Does the product verify your answer to Question 2? Use a complete sentence in your answer.

4. The population of the largest city you have ever been to is 1,594,323 people. How many times greater is this city's population than the population of your small town? Show all your work and use a complete sentence in your answer.

5. Write the numerator and denominator from Question 4 as powers of 3. Then use the rule from Lesson 9.2 to find the quotient. Does the quotient verify your answer to Question 4? Use a complete sentence in your answer.

9

Assignment

Name _____ Date _____

As Time Goes By
Zero and Negative Exponents

The metric system is often the preferred system for measuring because of the ease with which conversions can be made. The unit for measuring length is the meter (m).

1. Complete the table below that shows common metric units of length.

Unit	Number of meters	Number of meters as a power with a positive exponent	Number of meters as a power with a negative exponent
Millimeter	$\dfrac{1}{1000}$		
Centimeter	$\dfrac{1}{100}$		
Kilometer	1000		

2. Determine the number of meters that are in 100 centimeters. Use a quotient of powers and show all your work.

3. Determine the number of meters there are in 10 centimeters. Use a quotient of powers and show all your work.

4. Determine the number of kilometers there are in 10 millimeters. Use a quotient of powers and show all your work.

2008 Carnegie Learning, Inc.

9 ■ Assignments **149**

9

Assignment

Name _____ Date _____

Large and Small Measurements
Scientific Notation

Each of the following scenarios include a very large or a very small number. Write each number in scientific notation.

1. In 2002, the United States public debt was $6,228,000,000,000.

2. There are currently about 7,607,000,000 one-dollar bills in circulation.

3. A mole of hydrogen atoms contains 602,200,000,000,000,000,000,000 atoms.

4. The mass of a hydrogen atom is 0.00000000000000000000000000167 kilograms.

5. Pennsylvania's revenue in the year 2000 was $54,517,000,000.

6. A computer can perform an addition calculation in 0.00000031 seconds.

7. Every year, about 13,000,000 Americans visit the doctor because of back pain.

8. A pollen grain measures 0.0004 meters in diameter.

9

Assignment

Name _____ Date _____

The Beat Goes On
Properties of Powers

1. Identify the property that is used in each step to simplify the expression.

$$(9xy^2)(2xy)^{-3} = 9xy^2(2^{-3}x^{-3}y^{-3})$$

$$= \frac{9xy^2}{2^3x^3y^3}$$

$$= \frac{9xy^2}{8x^3y^3}$$

$$= \frac{9}{8x^2y}$$

2. Simplify the expression $\left(\frac{-2x}{y^4}\right)^2\left(\frac{10y}{6x}\right)^3$. Identify the property that is used in each step.

3. Find the volume of the teepee at the right using the formula

for the volume of a cone: $V = \dfrac{1}{3}\pi r^2 h$, where r is the radius,

h is the height, and V is the volume. Show all your work and use a complete sentence in your answer. Leave your answer in terms of π.

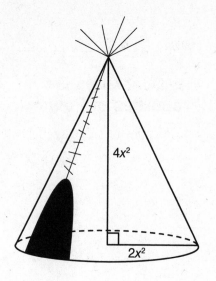

$4x^2$

$2x^2$

Assignment

Name _____ Date _____

Sailing Away
Radicals and Rational Exponents

Use the following scenario to answer Questions 1 through 3.

The period of a pendulum is the time the pendulum takes to complete one full swing. The period T in seconds can be modeled by $T = 2\sqrt{l}$, where l is the pendulum's length in meters.

1. What is the period of a pendulum that is 0.25 meters long? Show all your work and use a complete sentence in your answer.

2. What is the period of a pendulum that is 2 meters long? Show all your work and use a complete sentence in your answer.

3. How long is a pendulum with a period of 2 seconds? Show all your work and use a complete sentence in your answer.

4. Write two different expressions of the form $a^{1/n}$ that equal 4, where a is a real number and n is an integer greater than 1.

5. How do rational exponents help you to multiply or divide two radicals with different indices ($\sqrt[m]{a} \cdot \sqrt[n]{a}$ or $\dfrac{\sqrt[m]{a}}{\sqrt[n]{a}}$, when $m \neq n$)? Use complete sentences in your answer and include two examples to support your answer.

Assignment

Name _____ Date _____

Water Balloons
Polynomials and Polynomial Functions

Define each term in your own words.

1. polynomial

2. term of a polynomial

3. degree of a polynomial

4. Describe how the Vertical Line Test can be used to determine whether a polynomial is a function. Use complete sentences in your answer.

You use a sling shot and a rock to try to hit an apple on the ground. The rock leaves the sling shot with an initial velocity of 60 feet per second from a height of 5 feet off of the ground.

5. Use the Vertical Motion Model to write an equation that represents the height of the rock in feet.

6. Is your model a polynomial? If so, classify it by its degree and number of terms.

7. Identify each of the coefficients in your model.

8. What is the height of the rock after 1 second? What is the height of the rock after 2 seconds? What is the height of the rock after 4 seconds? Show all your work and use a complete sentence in your answer.

10

9. Complete the table of values that shows the height of the rock in terms of time.

Quantity Name	Time	Height
Unit		
Expression		
	1.0	
	2.0	
	2.5	
	3.0	

10. Create a graph of the model to see the path of the rock on the grid below. First, choose your bounds and intervals. Be sure to label your graph clearly.

Variable quantity	Lower bound	Upper bound	Interval

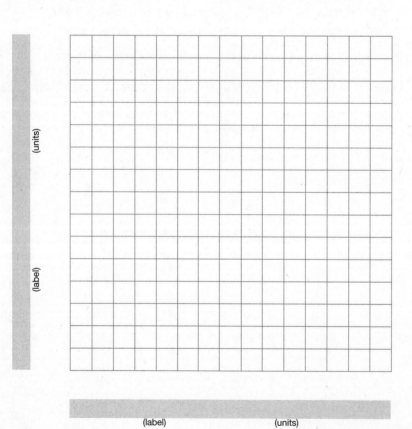

(units)

(label)

(label)   (units)

Name _____ Date _____

11. Use the graph and table to estimate the maximum height of the rock. Use a complete sentence in your answer.

12. Use the graph and table to estimate the time at which the rock will hit the ground. Use a complete sentence in your answer.

13. Is the polynomial a function? Use a complete sentence in your answer.

10

Assignment

Name _____ Date _____

Play Ball!
Adding and Subtracting Polynomials

The per person consumption of whole milk from 1980 through 2000 can be modeled by the function $y = -0.00023x^4 + 0.011x^3 - 0.146x^2 - 0.055x + 17$. The per person consumption of reduced fat and skim milk from 1980 through 2000 can be modeled by the function $y = 0.00038x^4 - 0.0166x^3 + 0.2045x^2 - 0.295x + 10.5$. For both functions, x is the number of years since 1980 and y is the per person consumption in gallons.

1. Find the per person consumption of both kinds of milk in 1990. Show all your work and use a complete sentence in your answer.

2. Find the total per person consumption of milk in gallons in 1990. Show all your work and use a complete sentence in your answer.

3. Write a function that you could use to find the total per person consumption of milk in gallons in 1990.

4. Use your function in Question 3 to find the total per person consumption of milk in 1990. How does the answer compare to your answer in Question 2? Show all your work and use a complete sentence in your answer.

5. Write a function that you could use to find how many more gallons of reduced fat and skim milk was consumed per person than whole milk. Show all your work.

6. Find how many more gallons of reduced fat and skim milk was consumed per person than whole milk in 1990 using your answers to Questions 1 and 5. How do your answers compare? Show all your work and use complete sentences in your answer.

Find each sum or difference. Show all your work.

7. $(2x^2 + 5x - 3) + (x^2 - 2x + 5)$

8. $(3x + 4) - (2x + 1)$

9. $(4x^3 + 2x^2 + x + 1) + (x^3 - 2x^2 - 1)$

10. $(7x^3 + 2x^2 + 5) - (6x^2 + 4x + 7)$

Assignment

Name _____ Date _____

Se Habla Español
Multiplying and Dividing Polynomials

A developer buys a large plot of land. She has plans to divide the land
into smaller lots and build houses on them. The houses will be built
in various styles and sizes, but the developer wants to follow certain
guidelines. The base of each house will be in the shape of a square.
Two optional upgrades are also available. The length of the house
can be extended by 8 additional feet for a rec room or the width of
the house can be extended by 12 feet for a sunroom or the length
and the width of the house can be extended.

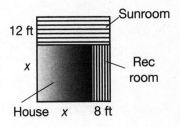

1. Write an expression for the length of the house, including a rec room.

2. Write an expression for the width of the house, including a sunroom.

3. Write a function for the area of the base of the house, including a rec room and a
   sunroom. Show all of your work.

4. Use the diagram above to calculate the area of the base of the house, including a rec
   room and a sunroom, when x is 24 feet. Show all your work and use a complete sentence
   in your answer.

5. Use your answer to Question 3 to calculate the area of the base of the house, including
   a rec room and a sunroom, when x is 24 feet. Show all your work and use a complete
   sentence in your answer.

6. How do your answers to Questions 4 and 5 compare? Why is it helpful to compare these answers? Use complete sentences in your answer.

7. Write an expression for the area of the rec room.

8. Write an expression for the area of the sunroom.

9. Write a function to find the percent of the total area of the base of the house that is rec room and sunroom. Show all of your work.

Assignment

Name _____ Date _____

Making Stained Glass
Multiplying Binomials

A manufacturer is designing and marketing swimming pools. The exact size of the pool varies depending on the buyer, but the pools are always made so that the ratio of the length to the width is 5:2. Each pool is also designed so that a 5-foot concrete walkway surrounds the pool.

1. Sketch a diagram of the pool described in the scenario above.

2. Write an expression for the total length of the pool, including the concrete walkway.

3. Write an expression for the total width of the pool, including the concrete walkway.

4. Write a function for the total area of the pool, including the concrete walkway.

5. Use the FOIL pattern to find the product in Question 4. Show all your work.

Find each product. Show all your work.

6. $(2x + 5)^2$

7. $(3x - 4)(9x + 1)$

8. $(5x + 4)(5x - 4)$

9. $(3x - 8)^2$

10

Assignment

Name _____ Date _____

Suspension Bridges
Factoring Polynomials

Your local zoo is building a tunnel for a new train ride. The tunnel can be modeled by the function $y = -\frac{5}{36}x^2 + \frac{5}{2}x$, where x is the distance in feet from the leftmost point of the tunnel and y is the height in feet of the tunnel. The train designers want the train to have the maximum height and width possible but be no more than 10 feet tall.

1. Write and simplify an equation that you can use to find the distance from the leftmost point of the tunnel when the height of the tunnel is 10 feet.

2. Multiply the equation in Question 1 by 36 to rewrite the equation with integer coefficients.

3. Use factoring to find the solutions of the equation in Question 2.

4. Based on the solutions from Question 3, what is the maximum width for the train? Use complete sentences in your answer.

10

Assignment

Name _____ Date _____

Swimming Pools
Rational Expressions

1. Write a rational expression in factored form with a first-degree polynomial in the numerator, a second-degree polynomial in the denominator, and a domain of all real numbers except 4 and 5.

When packaging products, companies want to use the least amount of packaging material possible. Finding the ratio of a package's surface area to its volume is one way to determine the efficiency of the package. The smaller the ratio, the better the efficiency of the package. A company makes a small box to hold its trial-size trail mix that is shaped like a rectangular prism with a square base. The company also wants to make a taller version of the box for the family-size trail mix.

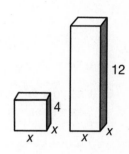

2. Find the surface area and volume of each box. Show all your work.

3. Write and simplify the ratio of the surface area to the volume, or the efficiency ratio, for each box. Show all your work.

4. Divide the efficiency ratio for the trial-size box by the efficiency ratio for the family-size box. Do not leave the resulting rational expression in factored form. Show all your work.

5. Compare the numerator and denominator of the rational expression in Question 4. From your comparison, is the value of rational expression less than or greater than 1? Use a complete sentence to explain your answer.

6. Use your answer to Question 5 to determine which trail mix box is more efficient. Use a complete sentence to explain your answer.

10 **Find each sum or difference. Show all your work and leave your answer in simplified form.**

7. $\dfrac{9}{5x} + \dfrac{5}{8x}$

8. $\dfrac{10}{2x^2} - \dfrac{3}{7x}$

9. Find the least common multiple of $4x$ and $4(x + 9)$. Use a complete sentence in your answer.

Assignment

Name _____ Date _____

Your Best Guess
Introduction to Probability

1. In your own words, explain the difference between the probability of an event and the odds in favor of an event. Use complete sentences in your answer.

2. What does it mean for an event to have a probability of 0? What does it mean for an event to have a probability of 1? Use complete sentences in your answer.

3. List several real-life situations where it would be helpful for you to have an understanding of probability.

A local weather forecaster has some bad news for the region. Based on historic data, she predicts that in April there will be 10 snowy days, 6 rainy days, 8 cloudy days, and 6 clear, sunny days.

4. Your big softball game is planned for April. What is the probability that you will have a clear, sunny day for the game? What are the odds that you will have a clear, sunny day for the game? Show all your work and use complete sentences in your answer.

© 2008 Carnegie Learning, Inc.

11

Chapter 11 ■ Assignments   **171**

5. Nothing makes your younger brother happier than splashing around in the mud puddles after a rainy day. What is the probability that any given day in April will be rainy? What are the odds that any given day in April will be rainy? Show all your work and use complete sentences in your answer.

6. Snowy days are not always a bad thing, because you can go sledding. What is the probability that you have a snowy day to go sledding on a given day in April? What are the odds that you have a snowy day to go sledding on any given day in April? Show all your work and use complete sentences in your answer.

Assignment

Name _____ Date _____

What's in the Bag?
Theoretical and Experimental Probabilities

1. In your own words, explain the difference between experimental and theoretical probability. Use complete sentences in your answer.

2. A bag contains 3 red marbles, 5 blue marbles, 8 yellow marbles, and 4 black marbles. What is the theoretical probability of randomly picking each color marble?

3. Perform an experiment by flipping a coin 10, 20, 30, 40, and then 50 times. Record the theoretical results and your experimental results in the table below.

Number of Coin Flips	Expected Number of Tails (Theoretical)	Actual Number of Tails (Experimental)
10		
20		
30		
40		
50		

4. Are the theoretical results always the same as your experimental results in the experiment in Question 3? Use a complete sentence in your answer.

5. Compare the theoretical and experimental probabilities for your experiment in Question 3. What can you conclude? Use a complete sentence in your answer.

11

Extension: Design Your Own Experiment

Design your own experiment to test how closely experimental probability compares to theoretical probability. The questions below will help guide you through the experiment.

6. Describe your experiment. Use complete sentences.

7. What materials will you need (for instance, marbles, number cubes, coins, scraps of paper)?

8. Create a table that will help you organize your data.

9. Calculate the theoretical probability of your event. Show all your work.

10. How does the experimental probability compare with the theoretical probability? Use complete sentences in your answer.

Assignment

Name _____ Date _____

A Brand New Bag
Using Probabilities to Make Predictions

Your sock drawer is a mess! You just shove all of your socks into the drawer without worrying about finding matches. Your aunt asks you how many pairs of each color you have. You know that you have a total of 32 pairs of socks, or 64 individual socks, in four different colors: white, blue, black, and tan. You do not want to count all of your socks, so you decide to randomly pick 20 socks and predict the number of each color from your results. Your results are shown in the table below.

Sock color	white	blue	black	tan
Number of socks	12	1	3	4

1. What is the experimental probability of choosing each color of sock? Use complete sentences in your answer.

2. Based on your experiment, how many of each color sock do you think is in the drawer? Show all your work and use a complete sentence in your answer.

3. Based on your answers in Question 2, how many pairs of each color sock are in the drawer? Use a complete sentence in your answer.

11

4. Your drawer actually contains 16 pairs of white socks, 2 pairs of blue socks, 6 pairs of black socks, and 8 pairs of tan socks. How accurate was your prediction in Question 3?

5. How could you increase the accuracy of your prediction? Use a complete sentence in your answer.

6. Would it make sense to perform 100 trials of this experiment? Use complete sentences in your answer.

Assignment

Name _____ Date _____

Fun with Number Cubes
Graphing Frequencies of Outcomes

You are playing a game that involves spinning two different spinners and moving around a board. Each spinner is divided into five equal regions labeled 1, 2, 3, 4, and 5. For each turn, you spin both spinners and add the two resulting numbers to see how many spaces you will move around the board.

1. What is the maximum number of spaces that you can move on one turn?

2. What is the minimum number of spaces that you can move on one turn?

3. Complete the table below to show the total number of spaces that you will move if each spinner lands on the indicated number.

		First spinner				
		1	**2**	**3**	**4**	**5**
Second spinner	**1**					
	2					
	3					
	4					
	5					

4. Create a line plot based on the results from the table in Question 3.

11

5. If you spin a sum of 6 on your next turn, you will lose a turn. If you spin a sum of 7, you will win the game. Which outcome is more likely? Find the probability of each and use a complete sentence in your answer.

6. On your next turn, what is the probability that you will move 4 spaces?

7. On your next turn, what is the most likely number of spaces that you will move? How do you know? Use complete sentences in your answer.

Assignment

Name _____ Date _____

Going to the Movies
Counting and Permutations

Simplify each expression by first writing each factorial as a product.

1. 4!

2. $\dfrac{4!2!}{3!}$

3. $\dfrac{10!}{8!}$

4. $\dfrac{6!}{7!}$

5. You look in your closet and see that you have 4 different pairs of jeans and 3 different belts. How many different jean and belt combinations do you have? Show all your work and use a complete sentence in your answer.

6. A local fast-food restaurant is selling meal combinations for $3.99. Each meal includes a sandwich, a side dish, and a drink. If the restaurant has 6 sandwich options, 4 side dish options, and 3 drink options, how many different meal combinations can the restaurant offer? Show all your work and use a complete sentence in your answer.

7. A computer manufacturer is refurbishing old monitors, keyboards, and CPUs. They have 5 types of monitors, 1 type of keyboard, and 2 types of CPUs. How many different computer combinations can the manufacturer offer? Show all your work and use a complete sentence in your answer.

Your baby sister is playing with four different lettered blocks. The letters on the blocks are E, B, R, and A. She is unable to read, so she is unable to consciously spell words.

   8. How many possible words can she spell? What are they?

   9. How many different ways can she arrange the lettered blocks? Show all your work and use a complete sentence in your answer.

   10. What is the probability that your sister will randomly spell a word? Show all your work and use a complete sentence in your answer.

11

Assignment

Name _____ Date _____

Going Out for Pizza
Permutations and Combinations

Find the value of each expression. Show all your work.

1. $_5P_3$

2. $_6C_4$

3. The principal is choosing four students to be recognized on the evening news for winning awards in a Martin Luther King essay contest. Seven students from your school actually won honorable mention awards for their essays. Find the number of different groups of students that can appear on the evening news. Show all your work and use a complete sentence in your answer.

4. A wedding planner must decide how to seat some of a bride's family members. Six seats are left in the front row and eight family members still need to be seated. Find how many different seating arrangements are possible for the front row. Show all your work and use a complete sentence in your answer.

11

5. Describe two real-life counting scenarios, one that would use permutations and one that would use combinations. Use complete sentences in your answer.

Assignment

Name _____ Date _____

Picking Out Socks
Independent and Dependent Events

Determine whether each of the compound events are independent or dependent.

1. You roll two six-sided number cubes and get a 4 and a 5.

2. You draw an ace out of a standard deck of cards and then, without replacing the card, draw another ace.

3. You randomly choose a blue marble from a bag, and then randomly choose a red marble after replacing the first one.

You and your best friend are picking plastic colored eggs out of a basket. A total of 10 eggs are in the basket. Only three of the eggs are filled with gift certificate prizes.

4. You choose an egg first. What is the probability that you will choose one of the prize-filled eggs?

5. Suppose you chose a prize-filled egg. What is the probability that your friend will also choose a prize-filled egg?

6. What is the probability that you and your friend will each choose a prize-filled egg? Show all your work and use a complete sentence in your answer.

11

7. Your favorite restaurant offers 3 types of burgers and 4 kinds of sodas. Your sister says that she will pick something up for you on her way home. What is the probability that she will choose both your favorite burger and your favorite soda? Show all your work and use a complete sentence in your answer.

8. If you are rolling two different six-sided number cubes, what is the probability that you will roll two sixes? Show all your work and use a complete sentence in your answer.

9. Your name is placed in a jar with 14 other names for a raffle. If your name is chosen, you will then spin a spinner to determine the prize that you will receive. The spinner is divided into six equal regions. Each region has a different prize listed on it, and the one grand prize is a laptop computer. What is the probability that your name will be chosen and you will win the grand prize? Show all your work and use a complete sentence in your answer.

10. You randomly choose four cards from a standard deck of cards without replacement. What is the probability that you will choose four aces? Show all your work and use a complete sentence in your answer.

11

Assignment

Name _____ Date _____

Probability on the Shuffleboard Court
Geometric Probability

1. Find the area of an 8.5-inch by 11-inch sheet of paper. Show your work and use a complete sentence in your answer.

2. Draw a 3-inch square "bull's-eye" in the center of your sheet of paper. What is the area of the square? Show all your work and use a complete sentence in your answer.

3. If you were to randomly drop an object onto the sheet of paper 10 times, approximately how many times would you expect it to land in the "bull's-eye?" (Assume that it always lands on the paper.) Use complete sentences to explain your reasoning.

4. If you were to randomly drop an object onto the sheet of paper 20 times, approximately how many times would you expect it to land in the "bull's-eye?" (Assume that it always lands on the paper.) Use complete sentences to explain your reasoning.

5. If you were to randomly drop an object onto the sheet of paper 300 times, approximately how many times would you expect it to land in the "bull's-eye?"(Assume that it always lands on the paper.) Use complete sentences to explain your reasoning.

11

6. Perform an experiment to test your answers. Draw a 3-inch square in the center of a sheet of paper. With your eyes closed, drop a paper clip from a height of about 2 feet onto the paper 10 times. How many times does it land in the "bull's-eye?"

7. Drop a paper clip 10 more times for a total of 20 trials. How many times does it land in the "bull's-eye?"

8. Compare the experimental probability from Questions 6 and 7 with the theoretical probability in Questions 3 and 4? Use a complete sentence in your answer.

9. Do you think this experiment can accurately test geometric probability? Why or why not? Use complete sentences in your answer.

Assignment

Name _____ Date _____

Game Design
Geometric Probabilities and Fair Games

You and your friends create a game for game night that is played with two number cubes. The game board consists of twenty spaces arranged in a square. On each player's turn, he or she rolls the number cubes. If the player rolls a sum of 7 or "doubles" (the same number on each cube), he or she moves forward two spaces. If the player does not roll 7 or "doubles," he or she moves back one space. The player to cross the finish line first wins the game.

1. Complete the following table of possible number cube rolls. Circle all rolls that would result in a forward move.

	1	2	3	4	5	6
1						
2						
3						
4						
5						
6						

2. What is the probability that a roll will result in a forward move? Show all your work and use a complete sentence in your answer.

3. What is the probability that a roll will result in a backward move? Show all your work and use a complete sentence in your answer.

4. If you roll the number cubes 15 times, how many of those rolls will likely result in a forward move? Show all your work and use a complete sentence in your answer.

5. How many spaces will you move forward as a result of the 15 rolls in Question 4? Show all your work and use a complete sentence in your answer.

6. If you roll the number cubes 15 times, how many of those rolls will likely result in a backward move? Show all your work and use a complete sentence in your answer.

7. How many spaces will you move backwards as a result of the 15 rolls in Question 6? Show all your work and use a complete sentence in your answer.

8. Is this a fair game? Why or why not? Use a complete sentence in your answer.

11

Assignment

Name _____ Date _____

Taking the PSAT
Measures of Central Tendency

Define each term in your own words.

1. mean

2. median

3. mode

The data below show the test scores for a ninth grade Algebra class. Jessica received a score of 71% on the test. She wants to analyze the data to see how her score compares to the scores of the rest of students in the class.

Ninth grade Algebra test scores: 61, 55, 71, 84, 58, 93, 82, 91, 47, 88, 84, 65, 46, 61, 84, 55, 69, 67, 73, 63, 37, 67, 72, 75, 73, 74, 95, 82, 73, 71

4. Create a stem-and-leaf plot of the data.

3	
4	
5	
6	
7	
8	
9	

7 | 1 = _____

5. What information about the data set can easily be seen after creating the stem-and-leaf plot? Use complete sentences in your answer.

6. Describe the distribution of the data. Use a complete sentence in your answer.

12

7. Analyze the data by finding the mean, median, and mode of the test scores. Use complete sentences in your answer.

8. Describe how Jessica's score compares to the scores of the rest of the students in the class. Use a complete sentence in your answer.

9. Describe a real-life data set for which the median is a much better representation of the data set than the mean. Use complete sentences in your answer.

12

Assignment

Name _____ Date _____

Compact Discs
Collecting and Analyzing Data

1. Given the data set below, your friend incorrectly states that the median is 111.
   Use a complete sentence to explain and correct your friend's mistake.

   313, 415, 111, 111, 612

   Ask six different people in your school, including at least one adult if possible, to rate five
   different school subjects based on the scale below:

This is one of my favorite subjects.	9–10
I usually like this subject.	7–8
This subject is OK.	5–6
I usually dislike this subject.	3–4
This is one of my least favorite subjects.	1–2

2. Record the responses in the table below.

School subject	Reviewer 1 rating	Reviewer 2 rating	Reviewer 3 rating	Reviewer 4 rating	Reviewer 5 rating	Reviewer 6 rating

12

3. Find the mean and median rating for each school subject. Record these measures of central tendency in the table below.

School subject	Mean rating	Median rating

4. Are the mean rating and the median rating close together for any of the subjects? Use a complete sentence in your answer.

5. In each case, which measure of central tendency is more representative of the overall rating of the subject? Why? Use a complete sentence in your answer.

6. Although a sample size of six is not really large enough to accurately represent the opinions of the students and staff at your school, what is one way you can try to make your survey as accurate as it can be? Use a complete sentence in your answer.

12

Assignment

Name _____ Date _____

Breakfast Cereals
Quartiles and Box-and-Whisker Plots

The table below shows the number of home runs hit by Babe Ruth for each of the 15 years he played for the New York Yankees.

Years	Home runs	Years	Home runs
1920	54	1928	54
1921	59	1929	46
1922	35	1930	49
1923	41	1931	46
1924	46	1932	41
1925	25	1933	34
1926	47	1934	22
1927	60		

1. Use the home run data to complete the table below.

Lower extreme	
First quartile, Q_1	
Second quartile, Q_2	
Third quartile, Q_3	
Upper extreme	

2. Use the information from the table in Question 1 to create a box-and-whisker plot.

3. Find the interquartile range for the home run data. Use a complete sentence in your answer.

4. Are there any data values that you would consider to be outliers? Why or why not? Use a complete sentence in your answer.

12

12

Assignment

Name _____ Date _____

Home Team Advantage?
Sample Variance and Standard Deviation

The table below shows how long patients had to wait to see each of two dentists who practice together.

Dr. Kent's wait times (minutes)	5	21	18	30	19	42	17	18	36	20	19
Dr. Mendoza's wait times (minutes)	20	45	6	19	18	5	40	39	21	44	8

1. Find the mean and the range of each data set. Show all your work and use complete sentences in your answer.

2. Can you draw any conclusions about the wait times from the mean and the range? Why or why not? Use a complete sentence in your answer.

3. How do you find the deviation of the set of data? Use a complete sentence in your answer.

12

4. Complete the table below. Round to the nearest tenth, if necessary.

Dr. Kent's wait times (minutes)	Deviation	Square of deviation
5		
21		
18		
30		
19		
42		
17		
18		
36		
20		
19		

Dr. Mendoza's wait times (minutes)	Deviation	Square of deviation
20		
45		
6		
19		
18		
5		
40		
39		
21		
44		
8		

5. Find the variance of the data for each dentist. Why is this information useful? Use complete sentences in your answer.

6. Find the sample variance for each dentist. Show all your work.

7. Find the standard deviation for each dentist. Show all your work. Round your answers to the nearest hundredth.

12

8. If you were a patient who desires the shortest wait possible, which dentist would you choose? Use complete sentences of explain your answer.

12

12

Assignment

Name _____ Date _____

Solid Carpentry
The Pythagorean Theorem and Its Converse

1. Tracks are being built along a large hill so that commuters can ride cable cars as they travel up and down the hill to and from work. What distance will the cable cars travel down the hill? Show all your work and use a complete sentence in your answer.

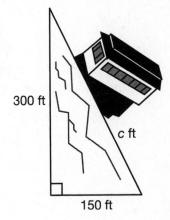

300 ft

c ft

150 ft

2. In baseball, the distance between each base is 90 feet. A runner on first base is attempting to steal second base. What is the distance that the catcher must throw the ball from home plate to second base? Label the diagram to illustrate the problem. Show all your work and use a complete sentence in your answer.

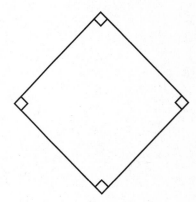

3. A carpenter places a 10-foot ladder against a wall so that the base of the ladder is 3 feet from the wall. How high up the wall does the ladder extend? Draw and label a diagram. Show all your work and use a complete sentence in your answer.

13

4. If you know that two sides of a right triangle have lengths 3 and 4, do you necessarily know the length of the third side? Use complete sentences to explain your reasoning.

5. Write your own word problem that can be solved using the Pythagorean Theorem. Solve your problem. Show all your work and use a complete sentence in your answer.

Assignment

Name _____ Date _____

Location, Location, Location
The Distance and Midpoint Formulas

Upon leaving your house, you travel 2 miles east to a park. After spending some time in the park, you travel 3 miles north to visit a friend.

1. Suppose the coordinates of your house are (0, 0). What are the coordinates in miles for the park?

2. What are the coordinates in miles of your friend's house?

3. What was the total distance that you traveled from your house to the park and then to your friend's house?

4. Use the distance formula to find the distance from your house to your friend's house. Round your answer to nearest tenth, if necessary. Show all your work and use a complete sentence in your answer.

5. Could you have also used the Pythagorean Theorem to solve Question 4? Explain the relationship between the Pythagorean Theorem and the Distance Formula.

6. Your school is located exactly halfway between your house and your friend's house. What are the coordinates in miles of your school? Show all your work and use a complete sentence in your answer.

Find the distance between each pair of points. Then find the midpoint of the line segment that has the given points as its endpoints. Round your answer to the nearest tenth, if necessary.

7. (4, 3) and (8, 5)

8. (–2, 4) and (0, 6))

9. (–10, –10) and (10, 10)

10. (2, 3) and (–4, –7)

Assignment

Name _____ Date _____

"Old" Mathematics
Completing the Square and Deriving the Quadratic Formula

Factor each trinomial.

1. $x^2 + 4x + 4$

2. $x^2 - 6x + 9$

3. $x^2 + 12x + 36$

4. $x^2 + x + \dfrac{1}{4}$

5. $x^2 - 8x + 16$

6. $x^2 + 2x + 1$

Solve each equation by completing the square and then extracting square roots. Show all your work.

7. $x^2 + 2x - 35 = 0$

8. $x^2 - 6x + 5 = 0$

Decide whether it would be better to solve each equation by completing the square or by using the quadratic formula. Use complete sentences to explain your answer.

9. $2x^2 + 5x + 1 = 0$

10. $x^2 + 12x - 13 = 0$

Name _____ Date _____

Learning to Be a Teacher
Vertex Form of a Quadratic Equation

Consider the equation $y = x^2 - 2x - 3$.

1. In which form is the equation given?

2. Write the equation in the factored form and vertex form.

3. Does the parabola open up or down?

4. What are the x-intercepts? Which form makes the x-intercepts easy to identify? Use complete sentences in your answer.

5. What is the y-intercept? Which form makes the y-intercept easy to identify? Use complete sentences in your answer.

6. What is the vertex of the parabola? Which form makes the vertex easy to identify? Use complete sentences in your answer.

7. Graph the equation.

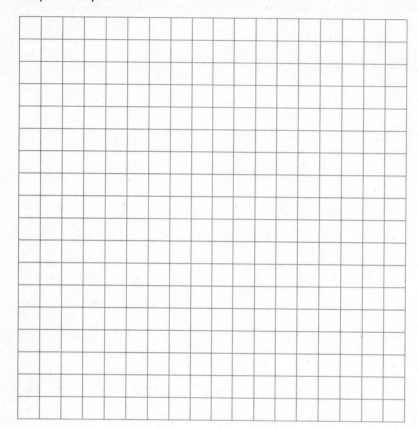

Rewrite each equation in vertex form. Then identify the vertex.

8. $y = x^2 - 4x + 2$

Vertex form: _____

Vertex: _____

9. $y = x^2 + 8x$

Vertex form: _____

Vertex: _____

10. In your own words, describe why it might be useful to be able to convert from standard form to vertex form to factored form.

Assignment

Name _____ Date _____

Screen Saver
Graphing by Using Parent Functions

Describe each transformation in your own words. Then give an example using the parent function $y = x^2$.

1. translation

2. dilation

3. reflection

For each function below, identify the parent function. Then describe the transformation on the parent function that will result in the graph of the given function. In some cases, there is more than one kind of transformation.

4. $y = |x| - 4$

Parent function: _____

Transformation(s): _____

5. $y = \frac{1}{2}(x - 3)^2$

Parent function: _____

Transformation(s): _____

6. $y = \frac{1}{4}x^2$

Parent function: _____

Transformation(s): _____

7. $y = |x + 1| - 5$

Parent function: _____

Transformation(s): _____

8. Graph $y = -(x + 4)^2 + 2$.

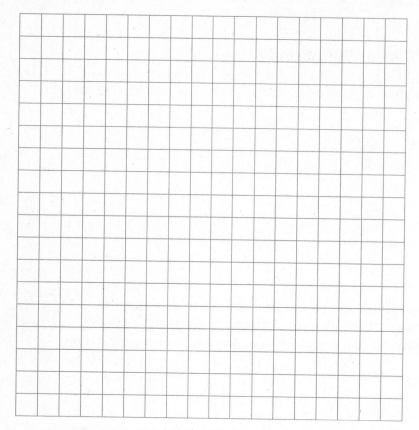

9. Challenge A parabola was reflected over the *x*-axis, stretched by a factor of $\frac{1}{2}$, and shifted 5 units to the left and 4 units down. After the transformations, the equation of the parabola is $y = -\frac{1}{2}(x + 2)^2 - 4$. What was the equation of the original parabola before the transformations?

Assignment

Name _____ Date _____

Science Fair
Introduction to Exponential Functions

In an experiment for the science fair at your school, you record the following data for the death phase of bacterial growth.

Time since beginning of death phase (in hours)	Number of bacteria	Number of bacteria
0	4000	$4000\left(\dfrac{1}{2}\right)^{0}$
1	2000	
2	1000	
3	500	
4	250	

1. Assuming that the bacterial growth continues in this manner, how many bacteria will there be five hours after the beginning of the death phase? Use a complete sentence to explain how you found your answer.

2. Based on the expression for the 4000 bacteria in the first row of the table, write an expression for each number of bacteria. Record your results in the third column of the table.

3. Write a function that gives the bacterial growth in terms of time. Let y represent the number of bacteria and let x represent the amount of time in hours.

4. Create a graph that shows the bacterial growth as a function of time on the grid below. First, choose your bounds and intervals. Be sure to label your graph clearly.

Variable quantity	Lower bound	Upper bound	Interval

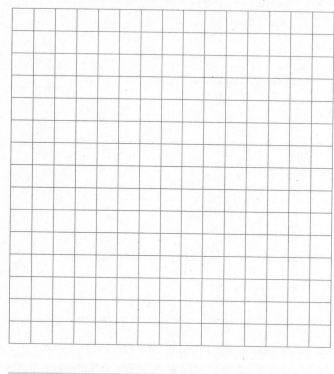

(units)

(label)

(label)   (units)

5. What is the y-intercept of $y = 4000\left(\dfrac{1}{2}\right)^x$? What does the y-intercept represent in the problem situation? Use a complete sentence in your answer.

6. How is the graph of the function $y = \left(\dfrac{1}{2}\right)^x$ different from the graph of the function $y = 4000\left(\dfrac{1}{2}\right)^x$? Use a complete sentence in your answer.

Name _____ Date _____

Money Comes and Money Goes
Exponential Growth and Decay

When you were born, your uncle deposited $1000 into an account that he hoped would help you pay for college. The account compounds annually at a rate of 4%.

1. The general formula for exponential growth is $y = C(1 + r)^t$. For the scenario above, write a function for the account balance over time and define the variables.

2. Complete the table below:

	Time	Account balance
Quantity Name		
Unit		
Expression		

3. Books and a meal plan at a local college are estimated to cost about $2000. When you start college at the age of 18, will your uncle's account fully cover this expense? Show all your work and use a complete sentence in your answer.

4. Suppose your uncle had invested only $750 in an account with a higher compound annual interest rate of 5%. Would the account have more or less money when you start college? Show all of your work and use a complete sentence in your answer.

5. The cost of tuition to the college of your choice for all 4 years is estimated to be $60,000. If your uncle wanted to pay your entire tuition by investing in an account that compounded annually at a rate of 4% for 18 years, how much would he have had to initially invest? Show all your work and use a complete sentence in your answer.

Consumers are often surprised by how quickly new toys, games, and gadgets become outdated. A popular computer model claims to depreciate in value at a rate of only 20% each year. The purchase price is approximately $1500.

6. The general formula for exponential decay is $y = C(1 - r)^t$. For the scenario above, write a function to represent the value of the computer over time and define the variables.

7. Complete the table below.

	Time	Value
Quantity Name		
Unit		
Expression		

8. Create a graph that shows the computer's value as a function of time on the grid below. First, choose your bounds and intervals. Be sure to label your graph clearly.

Variable quantity	Lower bound	Upper bound	Interval

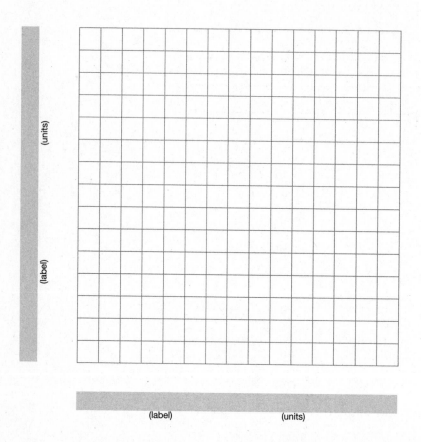

(units)

(label)

(label)   (units)

9. Use your graph to determine after what number of years the computer's value will be $100. Show all your work and use a complete sentence in your answer.

10. According to this model, will the computer ever be valued at $0? Use complete sentences to explain your reasoning.

Assignment

Name _____ Date _____

Camping
Special Topic: Logic

1. In your own words, describe how a mathematical statement is proven using a direct proof. Use a complete sentence in your answer.

2. In your own words, describe how a mathematical statement is proven indirectly. Use a complete sentence in your answer.

3. In your words, define counterexample. Use a complete sentence in your answer.

Decide whether each statement is true or false. If it is true, provide a proof. If it is false, provide a counterexample to prove that it is false. Use complete sentences in your answer.

4. Every time Jonathan goes to Little's Shoe Store, he buys a pair of sneakers. Jonathan came home with a new pair of sneakers, so he must have stopped at Little's Shoes on his way home.

5. $a^2 + b^2 = c^2$ is true for all triangles, where a and b are the lengths of the smaller sides and c is the length of the largest side.

6. Given three points A, B, and C on a piece of paper, the distance between A and B plus the distance between B and C equals the distance between A and C.

7. Multiplying two even numbers always results in an even number.

8. Prove the following statement indirectly.

   If x is an even number and y is an odd number, then $x + y$ is an odd number.